FUN with FONTS

Edited by *David E. Carter*

Fun with Fonts
First published 1997 Hearst Books International
1350 Avenue of the Americas
New York, NY 10019

ISBN: 0-688-15345-3

Distributed in North America by
Watson-Guptill Publications
1515 Broadway
New York, NY 10035
Tel: 800-451-1741
          908-363-4511 in NJ, AK, HI
Fax: 908-363-0338

Distributed throughout the rest of the world by
Hearst Books International
1350 Avenue of the Americas
New York, NY 10019
Tel: 212-261-6770
Fax: 212-261-6795

First published in Germany by:
NIPPAN
Nippon Shuppan Hanbai
Deutschland GmbH
Krefelder Str. 85
D-40549 Düsseldorf
Tel: (0211) 5048089
Fax: (0211) 5049326

ISBN 3-910052-95-9

Copyright 1997 by Hearst Books International and
David E. Carter

Printed in Hong Kong by Everbest Printing Company
through Four Colour Imports, Louisville Kentucky.

IN THE BEGINNING, THIS WAS SUPPOSED TO BE A FONT BOOK SHOWING SOME OF THE NEW "FUN" FONTS THAT ARE AVAILABLE FOR MACINTOSH AND WINDOWS COMPUTER APPLICATIONS.

BUT SOMEWHERE ALONG THE WAY, IT BECAME A LITTLE MORE THAN THAT.

"WHY NOT MAKE A FONT BOOK THAT'S ACTUALLY ENJOYABLE TO READ?" WE SAID.

SO, WHILE WE WERE DOING THE BOOK, SOME PRETTY NEAT LAYOUTS EMERGED. "HEY," WE SAID, "THIS BOOK HAS A LOT OF GOOD IDEAS FOR GRAPHIC DESIGN."

NOT TO MENTION THE FACT THAT THERE'S SOME PRETTY GOOD WORDS IN HERE.

WHILE WE USED SOME APPROPRIATE QUOTES FROM FAMOUS PEOPLE, MUCH OF THE FUNNY STUFF WAS WRITTEN BY **DAVID CARTER.**

TO BE FAIR, IT SHOULD BE NOTED THAT BOOK DESIGNER **SUZANNA M.W. BROWN** ALSO WROTE SOME PRETTY HUMOROUS (& intellectual & lyrical) COPY. BUT, SINCE **DAVID CARTER** IS EDITOR OF THE BOOK, SUZANNA'S NAME APPEARS HERE MUCH SMALLER THAN HIS. (SUZANNA, IF YOU WANT YOUR NAME IN LARGER TYPE, YOU'LL JUST HAVE TO GET YOUR *OWN* BOOK DEAL. SORRY. ANYWAY, YOU GOT *A NICE LISTING* AS BOOK DESIGNER. SO THERE.)

SO, THIS MAY BE THE FIRST FONT BOOK EVER WHICH IS (A) ALSO FUN TO READ, AND (B) HAS GRAPHIC DESIGN IDEAS WHICH YOU CAN EMULATE (FOOTNOTE: SEE "STEAL").

IF YOU'RE BROWSING THROUGH THIS IN A BOOKSTORE, HEY, GO FOR IT. IT'S *100%* GUARANTEED TO BE — A BOOK. SO BUY IT. AND HOPEFULLY, ENJOY IT — A LOT. HOPEFULLY, YOU'LL LIKE THIS BOOK ENOUGH TO DEMAND A FUN WITH FONTS, VOLUME 2, VOLUME 3, AND MAYBE EVEN MORE.

AND BE SURE TO TELL *ALL YOUR FRIENDS* ABOUT

Fun with Fonts

WHICH WAS

EDITED BY DAVID E. CARTER

AND

DESIGNED BY SUZANNA M.W. BROWN*

---

* DAVE SHOULD KNOW THAT THE BOOK DESIGNER CONTROLS TYPE SIZES!

Comic Book

ABCDEFGHIJKLMNOPQRSTUVWXYZ

ABCDEFGHIJKLMNOPQRSTUVWXYZ1234567890

Comic Book Two

ABCDEFGHIJKLMNOPQRSTUVWXYZ

ABCDEFGHIJKLMNOPQRSTUVWXYZ1234567890

DEAR MS. SHUMATE:

WE ARE RETURNING YOUR FAN LETTER.

ELVIS HAS LEFT THE PLANET.

Robotik

ABCDEFGHIJKLMNOPQRSTUVWXYZ

abcdefghijklmnopqrstuvwxyz1234567890

" Television will never be a serious competitor for radio, because people must sit and keep their eyes glued on a screen; the average American family hasn't time for it. "

The New York Times, 1939

Robotik™ is a Fontek font from ITC

Fashion Compressed

ABCDEFGHIJKLMNOPQRSTUVWXYZ
abcdefghijklmnopqrstuvwxyz1234567890

that's like comparing apples and oranges
cinnamon toasty Apple Jacks
as American as apple pie
don't upset the apple cart
she has little apple cheeks
Crabby Appleton——rotten to the core
The Apple Dumpling Gang
apple tree
apple crisp
Apple Computers
applesauce
apple blossoms
Apple Records
apple cider
apple of my eye
an apple for the teacher
an apple a day keeps the doctor away
road apples
one bad apple doesn't spoil the whole barrel
Johnny Appleseed
he's such an apple-polisher
everything's in apple-pie order

Fashion Compressed™ is a Fontek font from ITC

TFTwygmond-Light

ABCDEFGHIJKLMNOPQRSTUVWXYZ
abcdefghijklmnopqrstuvwxyz1234567890

TFTwygmond-ShadedLightItalic

ABCDEFGHIJKLMNOPQRSTUVWXYZ
abcdefghijklmnopqrstuvwxyz1234567890

I was sitting
And
He only talked to me for five minutes
I mean I
then
there
can get
you
IT JUST MAKES ME REALLY ANGRY
that kind of
have
completely
treatment
to pay
I waited and
for it!
waited and waited
at home
naked
I have to get a new doctor

TFTwygmond Bold, TFTwygmond-Light & TFTwygmond-ShadedLight Italic
are available from Treacyfaces

Toons

ABCDEFGHIJKLMNOPQRSTUVWXYZ
abcdefghijklmnopqrstuvwxyz1234567890

Laser Chrome

ABCDEFGHIJKLMNOPQRSTUVWXYZ

abcdefghijklmnopqrstuvwxyz1234567890

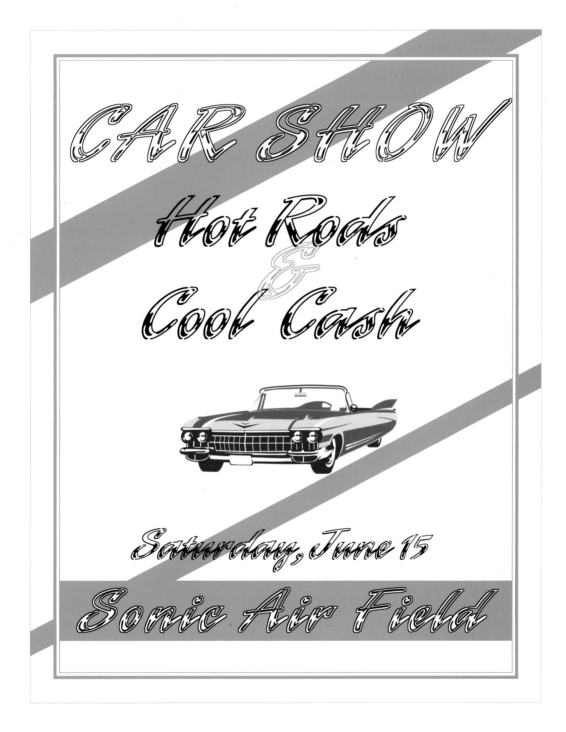

Laser Chrome™ is a Fontek font from ITC

Shatter

ABCDEFGHIJKLMNOPQRSTUVWXYZ

abcdefghijklmnopqrstuvwxyz1234567890

They SAID

it was a *nervous breakdown*

but I know a conspiracy

when I'm the

victim

of one....

Shatter™ is a Fontek font from ITC

TFZacron-Light

ABCDEFGHIJKLMNOPQRSTUVWXYZ
abcdefghijklmnopqrstuvwxyz
1234567890

TFZacron-Black

ABCDEFGHIJKLMNOPQRSTUVWXYZ
abcdefghijklmnopqrstuvwxyz
1234567890

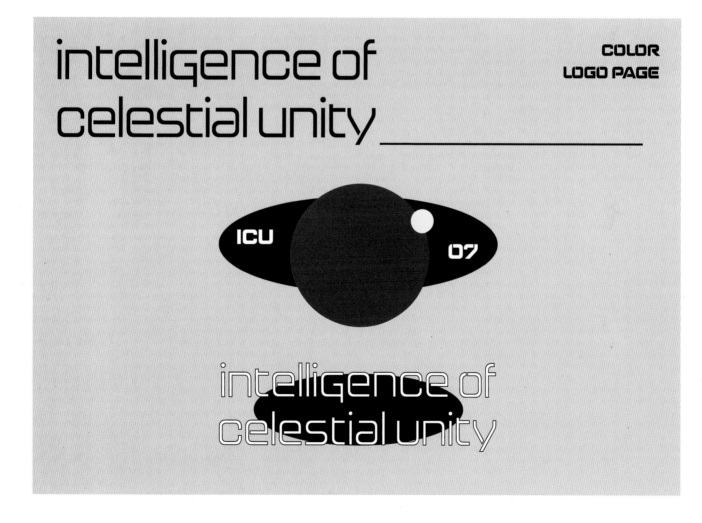

TFZacron-Black & TFZacron-Light are available from Treacyfaces

Cult

ABCDEFGHIJKLMNOPQRSTUVWXYZ
abcdefghijklmnopqrstuvwxyz1234567890

DOVE-SNAKES

Those dove-snakes are tricksy!
You has to watches 'em
That they don't gets too close.
They says they's harmless
But
Death follows 'em everyplace.
They smells of death
Under white feathers and silver scales.
They says they's friends
But
They wants you dead too!
Just looks at what they eatses—
Flesh and blood they says—
Flat bread and weak wine is all we sees
They even their cooks their coneys, *gollum*.

—Edgar Clayton

Cult™ is a Fontek font from ITC

ITC Bodoni Sev Swash—Book Italic

ABCDEFGHIJKLMNOPQRSTUVWXYZ
abcdefghijklmnopqrstuvwxyz1234567890

She smiled at him in that sultry way of hers with a rose between her teeth. She took the rose out of her mouth and placed it in a glass of water so it would stay fresh overnight.

She also took her teeth out of her mouth and placed them in a glass of water so they would stay fresh overnight.

ITC Bodoni™ Seventy-Two Book Italic Swash is available from ITC

Smack

ABCDEFGHIJKLMNOPQRSTUVWXYZ

abcdefghijklmnopqrstuvwxyz1234567890

One time...
When I was visiting my dad's oldest brother and his wife
some great words of wisdom were imparted to me.

We were sitting at the kitchen table
   looking at a box of family photographs
of picnics and holiday parties and various big to-do's
we used to have much more frequently.

Conversation waxed nostalgic
as we talked of those who
   were "no longer with" us
(by that time my dad had been in a nursing home about eight years)

You know I always had lots of fun
on their farm although we very rarely
DiD anything except sit around and talk
   or eat. That doesn't really have
   anything to do with the story.

My aunt commented on Dad's amazing constitution
being much like my grandma's — his mother's.
   She said that if only my grandma,
who died of congestive heart failure,
   had gone to the doctor,
instead of being too afraid,
she would probably still be alive.

Uncle Herschel said, "Well, Eula, I guess a lot of people
would still be alive if they hadn't died!"

   I've never forgotten that.

Smack™ is a Fontek font from ITC

DfUrbans

Creation As I Understand It
(an abridged version)

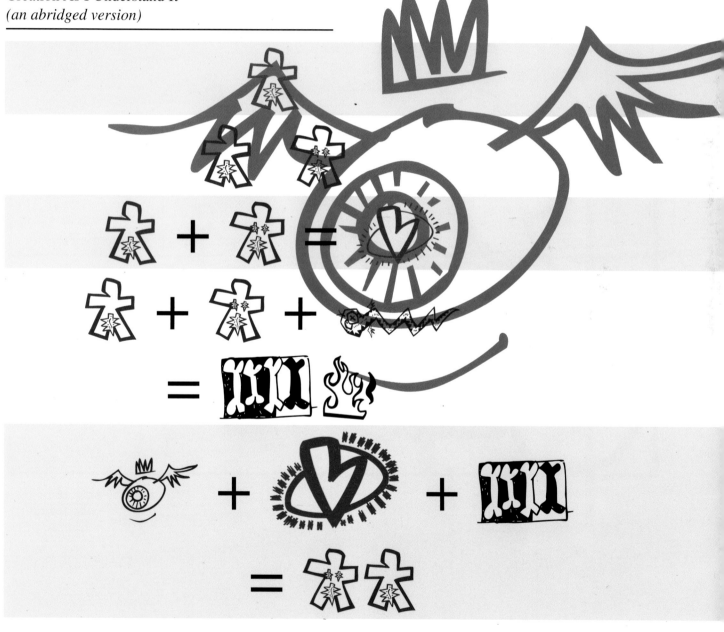

DfUrbans™ is a Fontek font from ITC

Rebound Demi

ABCDEFGHIJKLMNOPQRSTUVWXYZ
abcdefghijklmnopqrstuvwxyz
1234567890

Rebound Outline Bold

ABCDEFGHIJKLMNOPQRSTUVWXYZ
abcdefghijklmnopqrstuvwxyz
1234567890

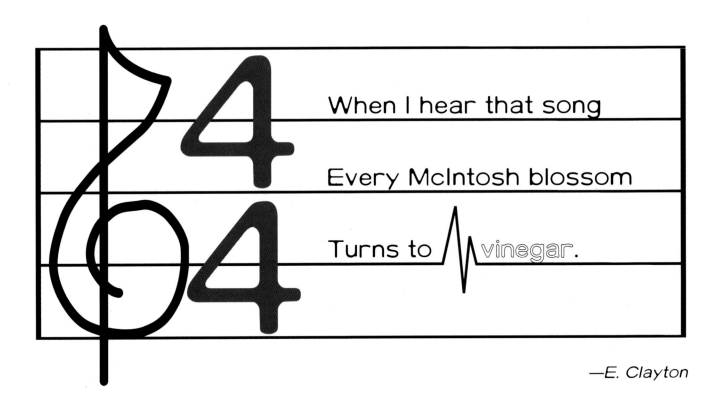

When I hear that song

Every McIntosh blossom

Turns to vinegar.

—E. Clayton

Rebound Demi & Rebound Outline Bold are available from Aerotype

ITC FarmhausNormal

ABCDEFGHIJKLMNOPQRSTUVWXYZ
abcdefghijklmnopqrstuvwxyz1234567890

Willie, with a thirst for gore,
Nailed the baby to the door.
Mother said, with humor quaint,
"Willie, dear, don't spoil the paint."

Into the family drinking well
Willie pushed his sister Nell.
She's there yet—the water kilt her
And we have to use a filter.

Willie fell down the elevator—
Wasn't found till six days later.
Then the neighbors sniffed, "Gee whizz!
What a spoiled child Willie is!"

Willie heard his sisters scream,
So he threw them in the stream,
Saying as he drowned the third,
"Children should be seen, not heard!"

Little Willie hung his sister;
She was dead before we missed her.
"Willie's always up to tricks.
Ain't he cute? He's only six!"

Willie split the baby's head,
To see if brains were gray or red.
Mother, troubled, said to father,
"Children are an awful bother!"

Willie poisoned his father's tea;
Father died in agony.
Mother came, and looked quite vexed:
"Really, Will," she said, "what next?"

—anonymous

ITC Farmhaus™ Normal & ITC Farmhaus™ Not So are available from ITC

Tag

ABCDEFGHIJKLMNOPQRSTUVWXYZ
1234567890

NOW ENTERING

PLEASE KEEP HANDS
INSIDE WINDOWS

PLEASE
DO NOT FEED
THE ANIMALS

PLEASE FEED
THE HUMANS

Tag™ is a Fontek font from ITC

Hemingway

ABCDEFGHIJKLMNOPQRSTUVWXYZ
abcdefghijklmnopqrstuvwxyz1234567890

Dear Mrs. Fahrquahr,

You were so kind to remember Robert and me on the occasion of our wedding. Words cannot express how touched we both were when we opened your very unique gift of a stuffed owl. Robert and I both agree that your good taste and thoughtfulness are directly reflected in your gift. Though we haven't yet chosen a site for our owl to "perch," we are keeping it safe from dust and light, wrapped in a plastic bag in our attic until we find the perfect spot it so fully deserves.

Thank you for being such a memorable part of our special day!

Gratefully,
Elizabeth

Hemingway is available from Great American Font Works

Ad Lib Font

ABCDEFGHIJKLMNOPQRSTUVWXYZ
abcdefghijklmnopqrstuvwxyz1234567890

Why do I like golf so much?

Maybe because it's so much like two of my favorite things from childhood: a walk in the woods, and an Easter egg hunt.

Meltdown

ABCDEFGHIJKLMNOPQRSTUVWXYZ

abcdefghijklmnopqrstuvwxyz1234567890

My mouth sweats for some of the cherry Kool-Aid we made last summer in your cabin by the lake.

Meltdown is available from Mind Candy

Chiller

ABCDEFGHIJKLMNOPQRSTUVWXYZ

abcdefghijklmnopqrstuvwxyz1234567890

When I was in grade school, I used to stay up late and watch this program on Channel 13 called "Chiller". It was old scary movies, and one night I heard someone say "serial killer".

I started laughing real hard because I thought of "cereal killer", and pictured someone shooting a box of corn flakes.

Ever since that time, I have loved to play word games.

Sometimes, when I do it, people look at me kind of funny.
But at least I'm not a serial killer.

Chiller™ is a Fontek font from ITC

Expose

ABCDEFGHIJKLMNOPQRSTUVWXYZ
abcdefghijklmnopqrstuvwxyz1234567890

In America, when a child says "I'm starving" it usually means a candy bar before a caloric nightmare of a dinner, half of which will be totally wasted and thrown in the trash.

The same phrase has a different meaning in Somalia, or Bangladesh, or Chile…

Expose is available from Olduvai

Arriba Arriba

ABCDEFGHIJKLMNOPQRSTUVWXYZ
abcdefghijklmnopqrstuvwxyz1234567890

Arriba Arriba™ is a Fontek font from ITC

VTypewriter-RemingtonPortable

ABCDEFGHIJKLMNOPQRSTUVWXYZ
abcdefghijklmnopqrstuvwxyz1234567890

VTypewriter-Royal

ABCDEFGHIJKLMNOPQRSTUVWXYZ
abcdefghijklmnopqrstuvwxyz1234567890

It was a dark and stormy night. If only he could see the road. But the battery in his Studebaker was dying and his lights were dim at best.

She was right he thought.

It was a stop sign plain and simple.

He reached in his pocket for a hand-kerchief and pulled out a .45!

And it galled him to think so.

He'd never forget the way she wore her red lipstick. After all, it nearly cost him his life.

"Got a light?"

And now Johnny was lying dead on the floor in a pool of blood that reminded him strangely of the spaghetti sauce Johnny's mother made every Friday.

"THAT'S LIFE IN THE CITY, BABY."

He blew smoke rings as he won-dered whether to call the cops or an ambulance. He chose the former.

Remember—he owed McGillacuddy a favor.

"The electric company called again, boss." Yeah, she was a good kid.

VTypewriter-Corona, VTypewriter-RemingtonPortable, VTypewriter-RemingtonPremier, VTypewriter-Royal, VTypewriter-RoyalDeluxe, VTypewriter-RoyalElite, VTypewriter-SmithUpright, VTypewriter-Underwood, VTypewriter-UnderwoodPortable, & VTypewriterRemingtonPerfected are available from Coniglio Fonts

ITC Humana Script Light

ABCDEFGHIJKLMNOPQRSTUVWXYZ
abcdefghijklmnopqrstuvwxyz1234567890

ITC Humana Script Bold

ABCDEFGHIJKLMNOPQRSTUVWXYZ
abcdefghijklmnopqrstuvwxyz1234567890

ITC Humana Script™ Light, ITC Humana Script™ Medium & ITC Humana Script™ Bold
are available from ITC

LCD Plain

ABCDEFGHIJKLMNOPQRSTUVWXYZ
1234567890

MY GRANDFATHER WORKED FOR THE
RAILROAD AND HAD THIS BEAUTIFUL
GOLD POCKETWATCH.

I ALWAYS LOVED THAT WATCH, AND
MY GRANDFATHER KNEW IT.

ON HIS DEATHBED, MY GRANDFATHER
CALLED FOR ME. "MY POCKETWATCH..." HE SAID TO
ME IN A FEEBLE VOICE.

I WAITED IN ANTICIPATION OF HIS NEXT WORDS.

"WANT TO BUY IT?" HE ASKED.

THAT'S WHY I HAVE A DIGITAL WRISTWATCH.

LCD™ is a Fontek font from ITC

Carbon 14 Regular

ABCDEFGHIJKLMNOPQRSTUVWXYZ
1234567890

FILES I'D LIKE TO SEE:

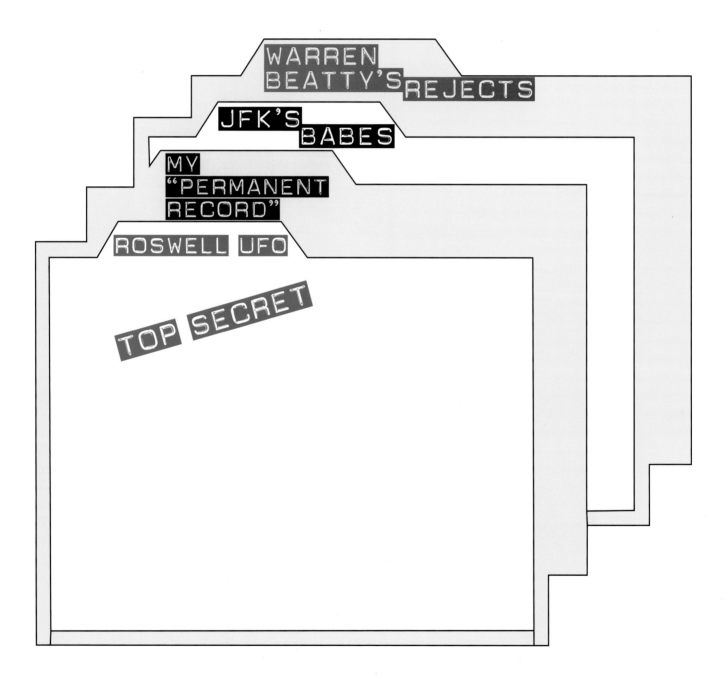

Carbon 14 Regular is available from Coniglio

Obsolete

ABCDEFGHIJKLMNOPQRSTUVWXYZ
abcdefghijklmnopqrstuvwxyz1234567890

Expletive Deleted

The quick brown fox jumped over the lazy *bleeping* dog.

Obsolete is available from Aerotype

Bevel Broken

ABCDEFGHIJKLMNOPQRSTUVWXYZ
abcdefghijklmnopqrstuvwxyz1234567890

Did you ever wonder what famous people were like when they were kids?

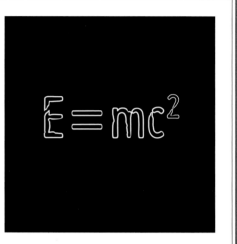

$$E = mc^2$$

I mean, did Einstein's mom ever say: "Albert, your room is a mess. Unless you clean up all of that clutter, you're grounded?"

I can just picture young Albert, confined to his room, thinking, "Einstein's Mom is a Crazy Square", and writing a formula for it.

Pablo Plain

ABCDEFGHIJKLMNOPQRSTUVWXYZ

abcdefghijklmnopqrstuvwxyz1234567890

And
how about
Picasso?

Did his teachers ever say to him:
"Pablo, unless you improve on your penmanship,
you're going to get held back this year!"?

Another thought: was Picasso any good at geometry?

Pablo™ is a Fontek font from ITC

Antigone

ABCDEFGHIJKLMNOPQRSTUVWXYZ
abcdefghijklmnopqrstuvwxyz1234567890

Antigone is available from Great American Font Works

TFBistro—Light

ABCDEFGHIJKLMNOPQRSTUVWXYZ
abcdefghijklmnopqrstuvwxyz 1234567890

FAVORITE
DOG
FANTASIES,
#36

The guy who lives at my house gets a stick and says, "Fetch."

I turn and look him in the eye. And in a precise British accent I say, "Fetch it yourself."

TFBistro—Bold &TFBistro—Light are available from Treacyfaces

Taiwan

ABCDEFGHIJKLMNOPQRSTUVWXYZ
abcdefghijklmnopqrstuvwxyz1234567890

The Kamikaze Restaurant

sushi served fresh daily
(or until it's all gone)

Freak

ABCDEFGHIJKLMNOPQRSTUVWXYZ

ABCDEFGHIJKLMNOPQRSTUVWXYZ1234567890

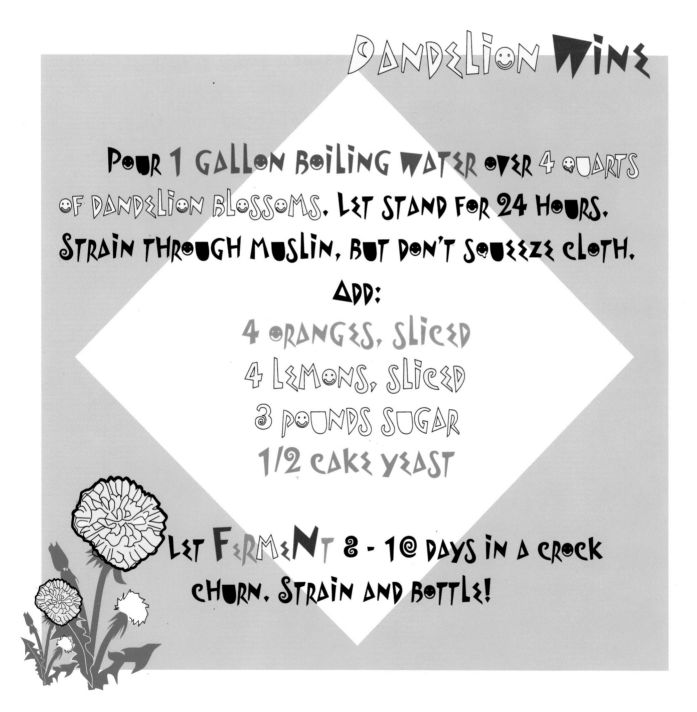

DANDELION WINE

POUR 1 GALLON BOILING WATER OVER 4 QUARTS
OF DANDELION BLOSSOMS. LET STAND FOR 24 HOURS.
STRAIN THROUGH MUSLIN, BUT DON'T SQUEEZE CLOTH.
ADD:
4 ORANGES, SLICED
4 LEMONS, SLICED
3 POUNDS SUGAR
1/2 CAKE YEAST

LET FERMENT 8 - 10 DAYS IN A CROCK
CHURN. STRAIN AND BOTTLE!

Freak is available from Olduvai

Maria

ABCDEFGHIJKLMNOPQRSTUVWXYZ

abcdefghijklmnopqrstuvwxyz1234567890

Fido did NOT like the new dog. Fido did NOT like the new cat. The dog was too big, the cat was too hairy, and they both smelled like animals.

Thriller

ABCDEFGHIJKLMNOPQRSTUVWXYZ

ABCDEFGHIJKLMNOPQRSTUVWXYZ1234567890

YOUR PRESENCE IS REQUESTED

FRIDAY

OCTOBER 13

AT 6:45 P.M.

TO AID IN THE SOLUTION

OF A MURDER

MURDER MYSTERY PARTY

AT

LEZLIE & TONY'S
(THE SCENE OF THE CRIME)

Thriller is available from Olduvai

Akira

ABCDEFGHIJKLMNOPQRSTUVWXYZ
ABCDEFGHIJKLMNOPQRSTUVWXYZ1234567890

IF ONE MORE
PASTEL LANDSCAPE
IS GOING TO
MAKE YOU
SCREAM...

MAYNARD CALLIS
227 E. MAIN STREET
MADISON, IN 47250

FOR WATERCOLORS THAT
ARE OUT OF THE ORDINARY

Akira is available from Olduvai

Radical

ABCDEFGHIJKLMNOPQRSTUVWXYZ
abcdefghijklmnopqrstuvwxyz1234567890

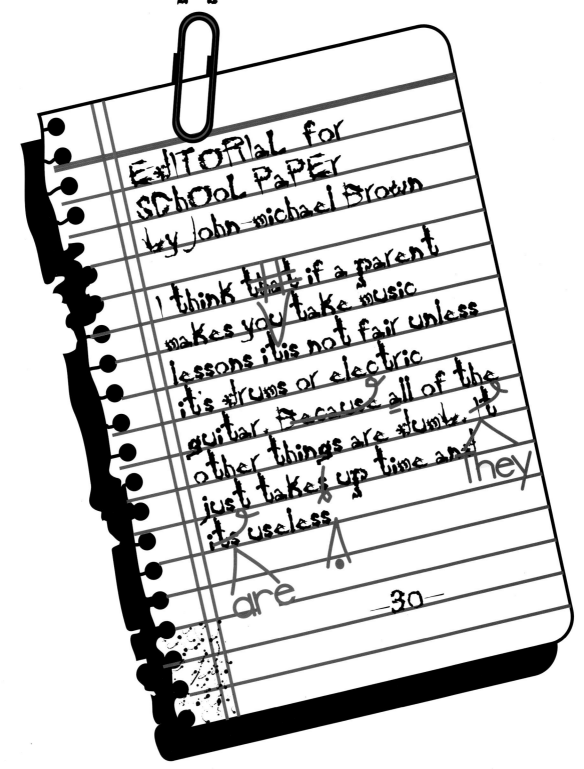

Radical is available from Great American Font Works

TFNeueNeuland OSF—Medium

ABCDEFGHIJKLMNOPQRSTUVWXYZ
abcdefghijklmnopqrstuvwxyz1234567890

TFNeueNeuland OSF—Inline Solid

ABCDEFGHIJKLMNOPQRSTUVWXYZ
abcdefghijklmnopqrstuvwxyz1234567890

I'm out **walking by myself**, and I see the **Dog Catcher**.

I get real close to him and he starts chasing me. He thinks I'm running at full speed, so he **lunges** with his net.

At that moment, **I turn on the burners** and leave him behind, flat on the street.

Did you ever see a dog **smile**?

TFNeueNeuland OSF—Bold, TFNeueNeuland OSF—Book, TFNeueNeuland OSF—Demi, TFNeueNeuland OSF—Inline Solid, TFNeueNeuland OSF—Light, TFNeueNeuland OSF—Medium, & TFNeueNeuland OSF—Solid are available from Treacyfaces

Jazz

ABCDEFGHIJKLMNOPQRSTUVWXYZ
abcdefghijklmnopqrstuvwxyz
1234567890

THE Gatsby COFFEE BAR

Jazz™ is a Fontek font from ITC

Chromium One

ABCDEFGHIJKLMNOPQRSTUVWXYZ
1234567890

HARD AND COLD AS
STEEL IN THE BLIZZARD
OF '78,
HIS HEART WAS THE
SAME.

I MIGHT HAVE BEEN ABLE
TO SEE IT SO
IF IT HADN'T BEEN FOR
THE HORRENDOUS
WEATHER THAT YEAR.

Chromium One™ is a Fontek font from ITC

Dancin

ABCDEFGHIJKLMNOPQRSTUVWXYZ
abcdefghijklmnopqrstuvwxyz 1234567890

Little-known facts about Dogs

- Outside dogs really resent inside dogs

- "Sniffing" other dogs is actually governed by strict rules of etiquette

- Really small dogs are actually cats in drag

Dancin™ is a Fontek font from ITC

Telegram

ABCDEFGHIJKLMNOPQRSTUVWXYZ
abcdefghijklmnopqrstuvwxyz1234567890

It was spring break of his freshman year, and he had just turned 18. He went to the beach with high hopes. Instead, a big 190-pound bully with bulging muscles kicked sand in his face, ruining his chances with the girls.

For a whole year, he pumped iron. He took food supplements to gain weight. And by spring break of his sophomore year, he had bulked up to a muscular 190 pounds.

When he got to the beach, he discovered that the bully from last year had also been pumping iron and he had grown to 225 pounds. The bully again kicked sand in his face, ruining his chances with the girls.

During spring break of his junior year, he decided to stay back at school and work on his term paper.

Telegram™ is a Fontek font from ITC

ITC Beesknees

ABCDEFGHIJKLMNOPQRSTUVWXYZ
ABCDEFGHIJKLMNOPQRSTUVWXYZ 1234567890

ONE OF THE GREAT
PROBLEMS OF OUR MODERN
AGE:

HOW
DO SANITATION
WORKERS KNOW
IF YOU'RE THROWING AWAY THOSE
OLD GARBAGE CANS?

Bitmax

ABCDEFGHIJKLMNOPQRSTUVWXYZ
1234567890

"HELLO...HI!
HOW ARE YOU?...YEAH?...
OH, WAIT A MINUTE. I'D
LOVE TO TALK, BUT...I'M
THE MACHINE!! GUESS
YOU'LL HAVE TO LEAVE A
MESSAGE AT THE BEEP!"

Bitmax™ is a Fontek font from ITC

ITC Blackadder

ABCDEFGHIJKLMNOPQRSTUVWXYZ

abcdefghijklmnopqrstuvwxyz 1234567890

My wife
and I went into
Westminster Abbey,
a damp, moldy place
where many English kings
are buried.
Almost immediately,
I began sneezing.
One of the guards said,
"Oh, you must be allergic to
"Dead King
Dust".

In America, we
would have simply
said, "Bless you."

ITC Blackadder™ is available from ITC

Lino Cut

ABCDEFGHIJKLMNOPQRSTUVWXYZ
abcdefghijklmnopqrstuvwxyz 1234567890

"I am sure the grapes are sour . . . "

It is easy to despise what you cannot get.

Aesop
The Fox and the Grapes

Lino Cut™ is a Fontek font from ITC

Chipper

ABCDEFGHIJKLMNOPQRSTUVWXYZ

abcdefghijklmnopqrstuvwxyz1234567890

Chipper™ is a Fontek font from ITC

ITC Jaft Roman

ABCDEFGHIJKLMNOPQRSTUVWXYZ

abcdefghijklmnopqrstuvwxyz1234567890

Follow...

...the

Drinking

Gourd

ITC Jaft Roman™ is available from ITC

Montage

ABCDEFGHIJKLMNOPQRSTUVWXYZ
1234567890

IT'S
ALWAYS DARK

WHEN YOUR
MIND IS CLOSED

Montage™ is a Fontek font from ITC

Pneuma

ABCDEFGHIJKLMNOPQRSTUVWXYZ
1234567890

THE FAMOUS SAWING-A-DOG-IN-HALF ILLUSION
ACTUALLY USES TWO DOGS

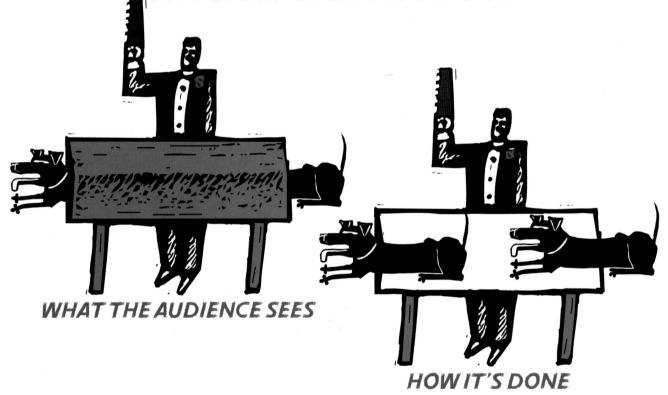

WHAT THE AUDIENCE SEES

HOW IT'S DONE

Pneuma™ is a Fontek font from ITC

Rubber Stamp

ABCDEFGHIJKLMNOPQRSTUVWXYZ
1234567890

This page is dedicated to Stan Freberg, from whom this line was stolen.

Rubber Stamp™ is a Fontek font from ITC

Scruff

ABCDEFGHIJKLMNOPQRSTUVWXYZ

abcdefghijklmnopqrstuvwxyz1234567890¤

"Hi! My name is Joe Kin and we're here at the skateboard track. When you skate here, you have to make a choice—either skate or die!!

"Here's the first lineup: on the inside, Crush, on the outside, Skull.

"Skaters, start skating!

"There they go. Whoa!!!!

Crush's wheel just hit a rock and he flew off his skateboard. He just DIED. Well, it looks like he made the wrong choice."

—J.W.B.

Frankfurter

**ABCDEFGHIJKLMNOPQRSTUVWXYZ
1234567890**

Frankfurter™ **& Frankfurter**™ **Medium** are Fontek fonts from ITC

Mastercard

ABCDEFGHIJKLMNOPQRSTUVWXYZ

1234567890

Mastercard™ is a Fontek font from ITC

Caslon with Swashes

ABCDEFGHIJKLMNOPQRSTUVWXYZ
abcdefghijklmnopqrstuvwxyz&1234567890

sugar	spice
heads	tails
Sodom	Gomorrah
Abbott	Costello
balls	strikes
AFL	CIO
work	play
day	knight
queen	king
Chuck	Di
love	hate
hearts	flowers
birds	bees
Playboy	Penthouse
top	bottom
Beavis	Butthead
dumb	dumber
haves	have-nots
Jack Sprat	his wife
Trinidad	Tobago
Cowboys	Indians
Roy	Dale
Siegfried	Roy
Lions	Tigers
Yankees	Mets
hot dogs	mustard
cake	pie
sugar	spice

Caslon™ Italic with Swashes is a Fontek font from ITC

Mekanik

ABCDEFGHIJKLMNOPQRSTUVWXYZ

abcdefghijklmnopqrstuvwxyz1234567890

Mekanik Italic

ABCDEFGHIJKLMNOPQRSTUVWXYZ

abcdefghijklmnopqrstuvwxyz1234567890

Scary Thought

Neither of the Wright Brothers
ever had a Pilot's License.

Mekanik™ & Mekanic™ Italic are Fontek fonts from ITC

Milano

ABCDEFGHIJKLMNOPQRSTUVWXYZ
abcdefghijklmnopqrstuvwxyz1234567890

Shocking

Watching women in furs,
I turn up my collar as the
wind worsens,
Thinking as I touch
the metal knob,
"Static electricity is
no respecter of
persons."

— E. Clayton

Milano™ is a Fontek font from ITC

Bang

ABCDEFGHIJKLMNOPQRSTUVWXYZ
1234567890

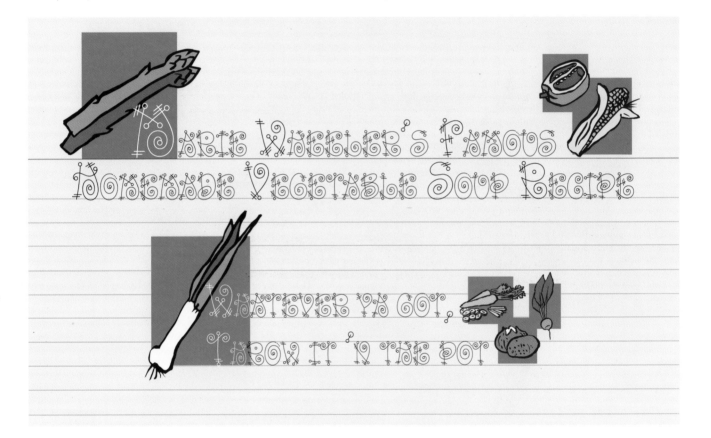

Mabie Wheeler's Famous Homemade Vegetable Soup Recipe

Whatever ya got, throw it in the pot

Paraphrased by Ed. Clayton

Bang™ is a Fontek font from ITC

NeonFont

ABCDEFGHIJKLMNOPQRSTUVWXYZ
ABCDEFGHIJKLMNOPQRSTUVWXYZ
1234567890

NeonFont™ is a Fontek font from ITC

ITC Odyssee Medium

ABCDEFGHIJKLMNOPQRSTUVWXYZ

abcdefghijklmnopqrstuvwxyz1234567890

ITC Odyssee Bold Italic

ABCDEFGHIJKLMNOPQRSTUVWXYZ

abcdefghijklmnopqrstuvwxyz1234567890

This is a <u>true</u> story

There was a ***beauty shop***
with a **taxidermist** next door.

I used to wonder what would *happen*
if someone went into the **wrong door**.

But
I never saw a *moose* with a
permanent, nor a *lady's head*
mounted in a den.

ITC Odyssee™ Bold, ITC Odyssee™ Bold Italic, ITC Odyssee™ Light, ITC Odyssee™ Light Italic, ITC Odyssee™ Medium, ITC Odyssee™ Medium Italic, & ITC Odyssee™ Ultra are available from ITC

Party

ABCDEFGHIJKLMNOPQRSTUVWXYZ

abcdefghijklmnopqrstuvwxyz1234567890

Another little-known fact about dogs

Q. Why do dogs dig holes?

A. Because they can.

Party™ is a Fontek font from ITC

Bertram

ABCDEFGHIJKLMNOPQRSTUVWXYZ
1234567890

Bertram™ is a Fontek font from ITC

Buzzer Three

ABCDEFGHIJKLMNOPQRSTUVWXYZ
1234567890

Buzzer Three™ is a Fontek font from ITC

Carumba

ABCDEFGHIJKLMNOPQRSTUVWXYZ

abcdefghijklmnopqrstuvwxyz1234567890

Carumba Hot Caps

ABCDEFGHIJKLMNOPQRSTUVWXYZ

ABCDEFGHIJKLMNOPQRSTUVWXYZ1234567890

FAVORITE _____

DOG FANTASIES, 545_____

The people who live in **my house** are gone. I walk to the OASIS, and discover that someone has made blue Kool-Aid®!

Carumba™ & Carumba™ Hot Caps are Fontek fonts from ITC

Faithful Fly

ABCDEFGHIJKLMNOPQRSTUVWXYZ
1234567890

"MEN ARE GENERALLY MORE CAREFUL OF THE BREED OF THEIR HORSES AND DOGS THAN OF THEIR CHILDREN."

— WILLIAM PENN

Faithful Fly™ is a Fontek font from ITC

ITC Digital Woodcuts Black

ABCDEFGHIJKLMNOPQRSTUVWXYZ
1234567890

ITC Digital Woodcuts Open

ABCDEFGHIJKLMNOPQRSTUVWXYZ
1234567890

KEITH PRESTON

ITC Digital Woodcuts™ Black & ITC Digital Woodcuts™ Open are available from ITC

ITC Bodoni Brush

ABCDEFGHIJKLMNOPQRSTUVWXYZ
abcdefghijklmnopqrstuvwxyz1234567890

GRADING THEMES

I will read you

Seven times seventy

With unforgiving eye

And red ink that

Never runs dry.

Edgar Clayton

ITC Bodoni™ Brush is available from ITC

Flight

ABCDEFGHIJKLMNOPQRSTUVWXYZ
abcdefghijklmnopqrstuvwxyz1234567890

Your representative owes you not his industry only, but his judgment; and he betrays instead of serving you if he sacrifices it to your opinion.

Edmund Burke

Flight™ is a Fontek font from ITC

Follies

ABCDEFGHIJKLMNOPQRSTUVWXYZ
1234567890

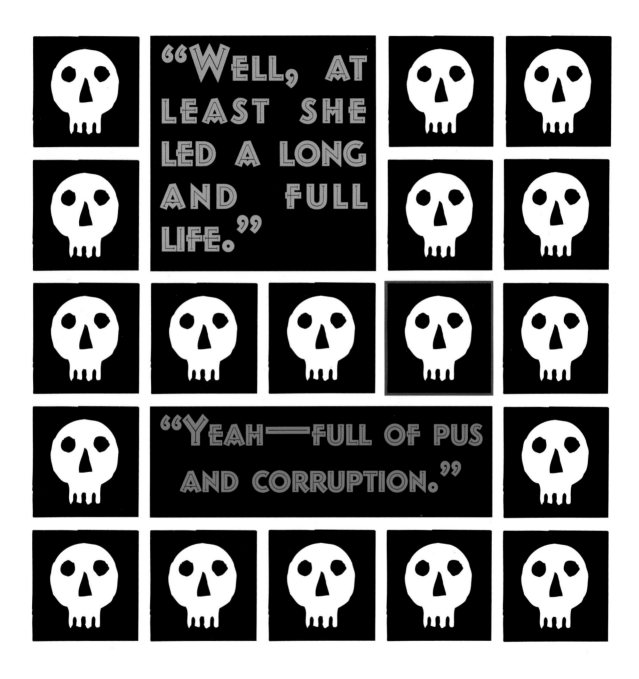

Follies™ is a Fontek font from ITC

ITC Isadora

ABCDEFGHIJKLM NOPQRS TUVWXYZ
abcdefghijklmnopqrstuvwxyz 1234567890

She's somebody's mother,
boys, you know,
For all she's aged and
poor and slow.

Mary Dow Brine
She's Somebody's Mother

ITC Isadora™ is available from ITC

ITC Jambalaya

ABCDEFGHIJKLMNOPQRSTUVWXYZ

abcdefghijklmnopqrstuvwxyz1234567890

ITC Jambalaya Tool

ABCDEFGHIJKLMNOPQRSTUVWXYZ

abcdefghijklmnopqrstuvwxyz1234567890

We are most nearly ourselves when we achieve the seriousness of a child at play. Heraclitus, philosopher

ITC Jambalaya™ & ITC Jambalaya™ Tool are available from ITC

Kanban

ABCDEFGHIJKLMNOPQRSTUVWXYZ
1234567890

THE BLACKNESS OF THE NIGHT
IS ALWAYS THAT.
AND WE GO ON
BEING AFRAID OF THE DARK.

Kanban™ is a Fontek font from ITC

Harlow Solid

A B C D E F G H I J K L M N O P Q R S T U V W X Y Z
abcdefghijklmnopqrstuvwxyz1234567890

" *Ladies,*
just a little more
virginity, if you don't
mind. "

Alexander Woollcott
Capsule Criticism (Beerbohm Tree to the Extras)

Harlow Solid™ is a Fontek font from ITC

Indigo

ABCDEFGHIJKLMNOPQRSTUVWXYZ

abcdefghijklmnopqrstuvwxyz1234567890

One would be in less danger
From the wiles of the stranger
If one's own kin and kith
Were more fun to be with.

Ogden Nash

Indigo is available from Aerotype

ITC Kick Italic

ABCDEFGHIJKLMNOPQRSTUVWXYZ
abcdefghijklmnopqrstuvwxyz1234567890

alternative openings for the Gettysburg address

- Eighty-seven years ago...
- A long time ago...
- Way back before most of us were born...
- Long ago, in a land far, far away...

ITC Kick™ Italic is available from ITC

Katfish

ABCDEFGHIJKLMNOPQRSTUVWXYZ
abcdefghijklmnopqrstuvwxyz1234567890

courir la gueuse

for that certain kind of woman!

Katfish™ is a Fontek font from ITC

ΛBCƆEFGHIJKLMNOPQRSTUVVXYZ
aBCDEFGHIJKLMNOPQRSTUVΨXYƷ1234567890

the mental health of millions of american adults could be greatly improved by simply eliminating one phrase:

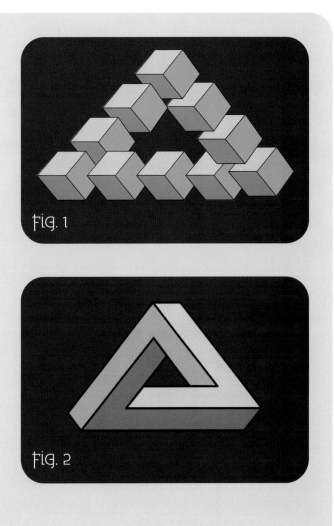

fig. 1

fig. 2

partial assembly required

Harvey

ABCDEFGHIJKLMNOPQRSTUVWXYZ
1234567890

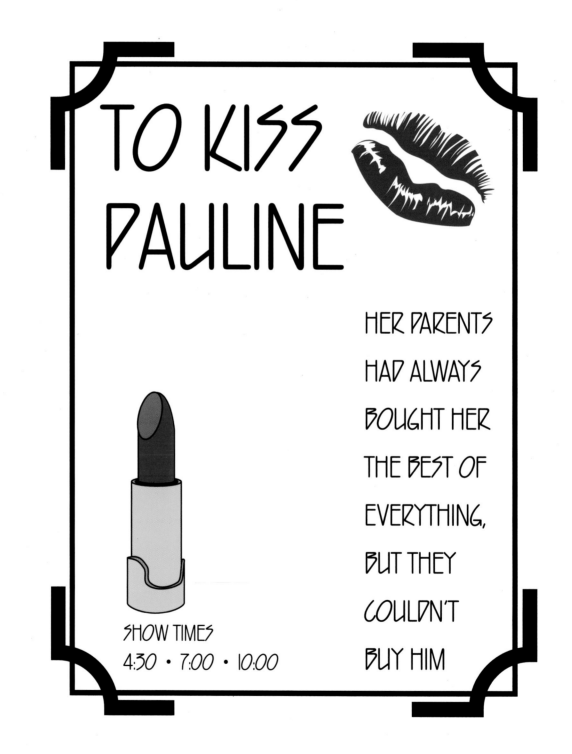

TO KISS
PAULINE

HER PARENTS
HAD ALWAYS
BOUGHT HER
THE BEST OF
EVERYTHING,
BUT THEY
COULDN'T
BUY HIM

SHOW TIMES
4:30 · 7:00 · 10:00

Harvey™ is a Fontek font from ITC

Hollyweird

ABCDEFGHIJKLMNOPQRSTUVWXYZ
abcdefghijklmnopqrstuvwxyz1234567890

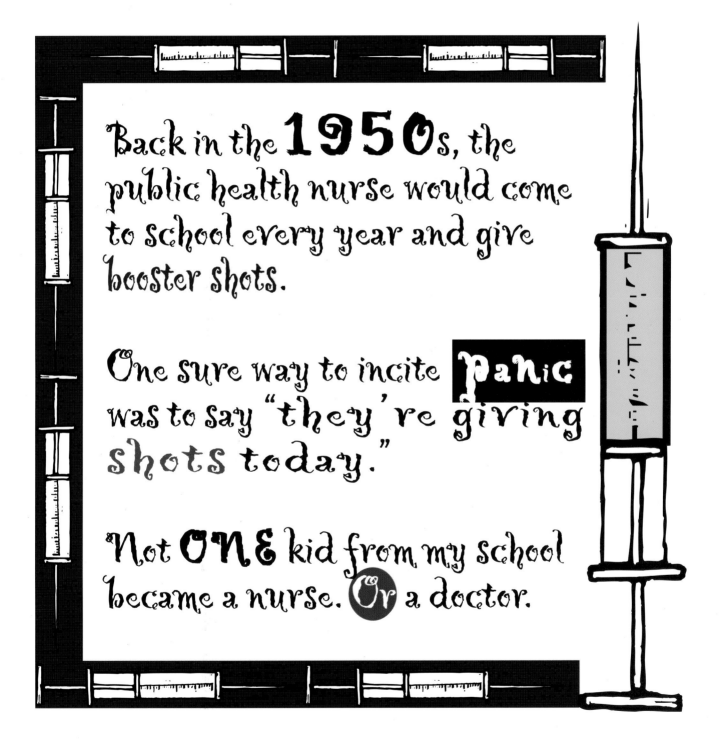

Back in the **1950**s, the public health nurse would come to school every year and give booster shots.

One sure way to incite **panic** was to say "they're giving shots today."

Not **ONE** kid from my school became a nurse. Or a doctor.

Hollyweird™ is a Fontek font from ITC

Frances Uncial

abcdefghijkLmnopqrstuvwxyz
1234567890

davies estate

to be sold at

his royal highness
the king's

auction
in the case of
forfeiture of back taxes
october 12
in the year of our Lord, 1763

Frances Uncial™ is a Fontek font from ITC

Synchro

ABCDEFGHIJKLMNOPQRSTUVWXYZ
1234567890

Synchro Reversed

ABCDEFGHIJKLMNOPQRSTUVWXYZ
1234567890

Synchro™ **& Synchro**™ **Reversed** are Fontek fonts from ITC

Khaki

ABCDEFGHIJKLMNOPQRSTUVWXYZ
abcdefghijklmnopqrstuvwxyz1234567890

The fever called
"Living"
Is conquered at last

Edgar Allan Poe
For Annie

Khaki is available from Aerotype

Mediterano

ABCDEFGHIJKLMNOPQRSTUVWXYZ
abcdefghijklmnopqrstuvwxyz1234567890

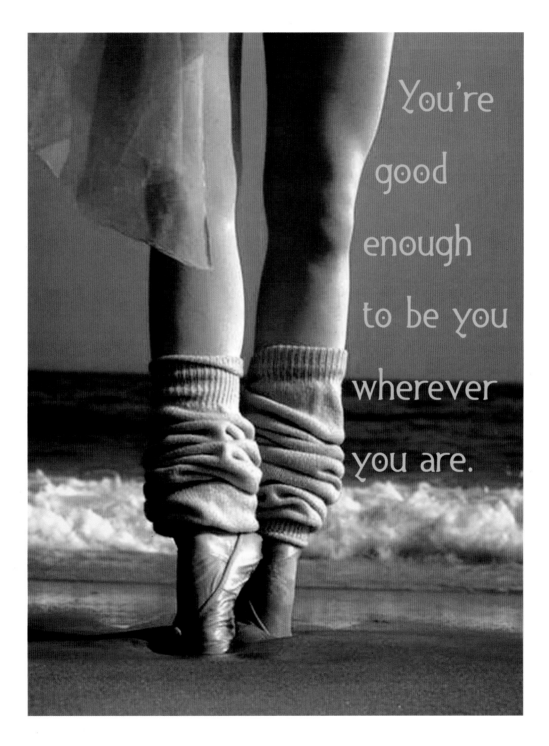

You're good enough to be you wherever you are.

Mediterano is available from Aerotype

Blast

ABCDEFGHIJKLMNOPQRSTUVWXYZ

abcdefghijklmnopqrstuvwxyz1234567890

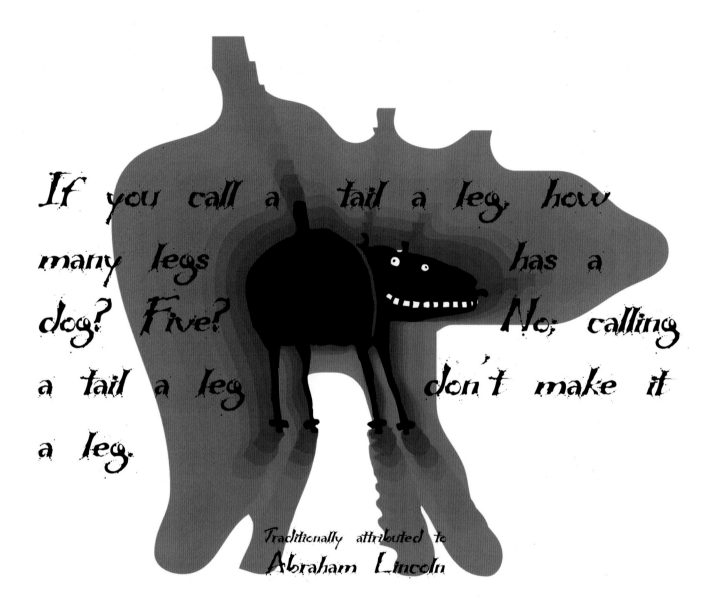

If you call a tail a leg, how many legs has a dog? Five? No; calling a tail a leg don't make it a leg.

Traditionally attributed to Abraham Lincoln

Blast is available from Olduvai

Dixieland

ABCDEFGHIJKLMNOPQRSTUVWXYZ

abcdefghijklmnopqrstuvwxyz

1234567890

She took to telling the truth; she said she was forty-two and five months.

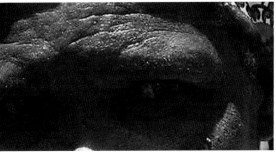

It may have been pleasing to the angels, but her elder sister was not gratified.

Hector Hugh Munro
"Saki"

Dixieland is available from Olduvai

Persuasive

A B C D E F G H I J K L M N O P Q R S T U V W X Y Z

a b c d e f g h i j k l m n o p q r s t u v w x y z 1 2 3 4 5 6 7 8 9 0

Gigi

ABCDEFGHIJKLMNOPQRSTUVWXYZ

abcdefghijklmnopqrstuvwxyz1234567890

I used to take walks with my dad sometimes after it rained. There was a beautiful tree-lined avenue he frequented and as we'd pass a low-hanging branch he'd say, "Why don't you grab that leaf for me?" Eager to please, with my puppy dog eyes, I'd grab that special leaf for my dad and immediately be doused with cold rainwater.

Not so long ago, my brother was making fun of me concerning that event. He thought I should've been able to see what was coming. But the joke's really on him. I only fell for it twice—three times tops!

Gigi™ is a Fontek font from ITC

Jokerman

ABCDEFGHIJKLMNOPQRSTUVWXYZ
abcdefghijklmnopqrstuvwxyz1234567890

Say not you know another entirely, till you have divided an inheritance with him.

Johann Kaspar Lavater

Jokerman™ is a Fontek font from ITC

Phobos

ABCDEFGHIJKLMNOPQRSTUVWXYZ
ABCDEFGHIJKLMNOPQRSTUVWXYZ1234567890

PEOPLE WHO WANT TO UNDERSTAND DEMOCRACY SHOULD SPEND LESS TIME IN THE LIBRARY WITH ARISTOTLE AND MORE TIME ON THE BUSES AND IN THE SUBWAY.

SIMEON STRUNSKY

Phobos is available from Olduvai

ITC Juice

ABCDEFGHIJKLMNOPQRSTUVWXYZ

abcdefghijklmnopqrstuvwxyz1234567890

And a

MOUSE

is miracle enough to

stagger sextillions

of infidels.

Walt Whitman

ITC Juice™ is available from ITC

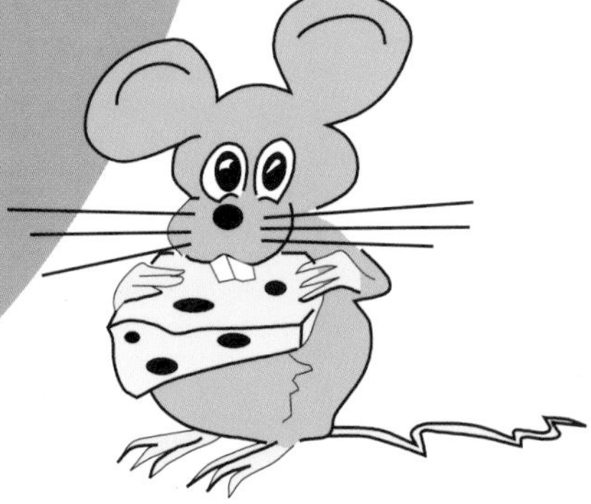

Privacy

ΑΒCDEFGHIJKLMNOPQRSTUVWXYZ
ΑΒCDEFGHIJKLMNOPQRSTUVWXYZ1234567890

Privacy is available from Olduvai

Mo Funky Fresh

ABCDEFGHIJKLMNOPQRSTUVWXYZ
1234567890

If 👁 COULD LIVE IN ANOTHER PERIOD OF HISTORY,
I WOULD LIVE IN THE 60s BECAUSE THEY HAD AWESOME CARS...
AND THEY HAD ALL KINDS OF GREAT HANGOUT PLACES. THE 👤 WORE THEIR 👕 WITH THEIR 🚬 ROLLED UP IN THEIR SLEEVE. AND THEY PLAYED AWESOME 🎸 AND WHEN YOU WOULD BE AT A 🚦, SOME GUY WOULD COME UP TO YA AND SAY, "YA WANNA 🏁?" AND YOU 🏁 AND HOPE YOU WOULDN'T GET CAUGHT.

—John-M

Mo Funky Fresh™ is a Fontek font from ITC

Princetown

ABCDEFGHIJKLMNOPQRSTUVWXYZ
1234567890

FAVORITE COLLEGE
FIGHT SONGS

SO YOU'RE AHEAD OF US BY 23
BUT YOU'LL NEVER BEAT
OUR S.A.T.

KICK 'EM, GOUGE 'EM,
SPIT IN THEIR EYE.
WE HAVE THE BEST
TEAM MONEY CAN BUY.

Princetown™ is a Fontek font from ITC

Retro Bold

ABCDEFGHIJKLMNOPQRSTUVWXYZ
1234567890

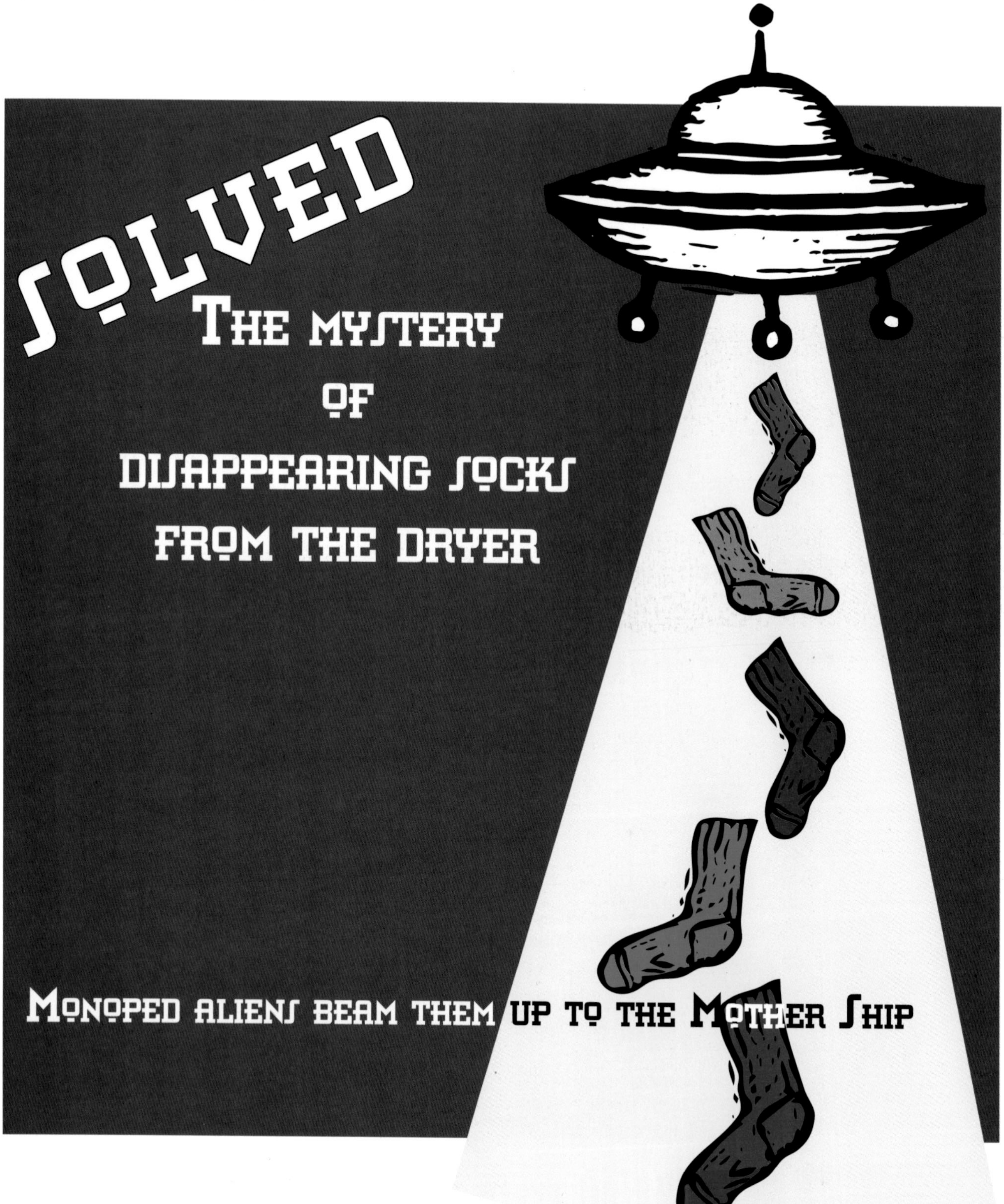

SOLVED
THE MYSTERY
OF
DISAPPEARING SOCKS
FROM THE DRYER

MONOPED ALIENS BEAM THEM UP TO THE MOTHER SHIP

Retro Bold™ is a Fontek font from ITC

Riva

ABCDEFGHIJKLMNOPQRSTUVWXYZ
abcdefghijklmnopqrstuvwxyz1234567890

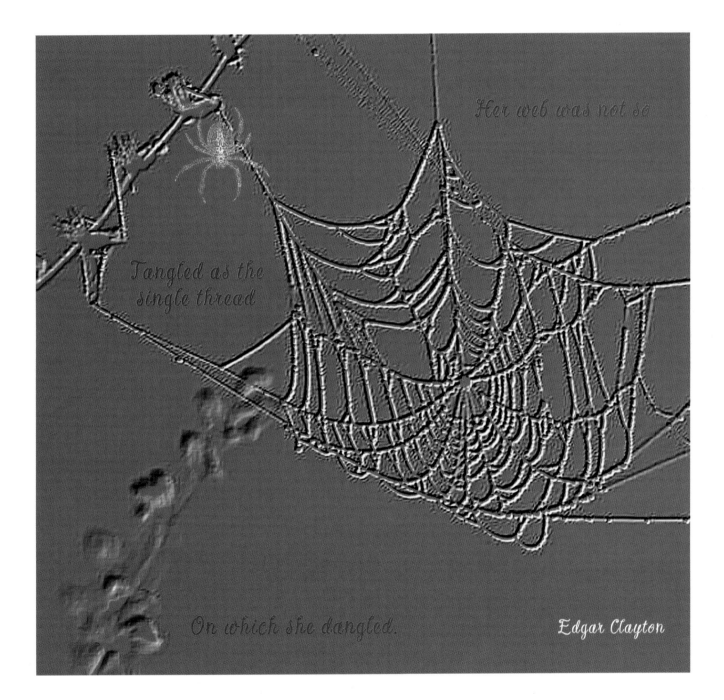

Her web was not so

Tangled as the
single thread

On which she dangled.

Edgar Clayton

Riva™ is a Fontek font from ITC

Shaman

ABCDEFGHIJKLMNOPQRSTUVWXYZ
1234567890

WHY BOWLING IS BETTER THAN GOLF

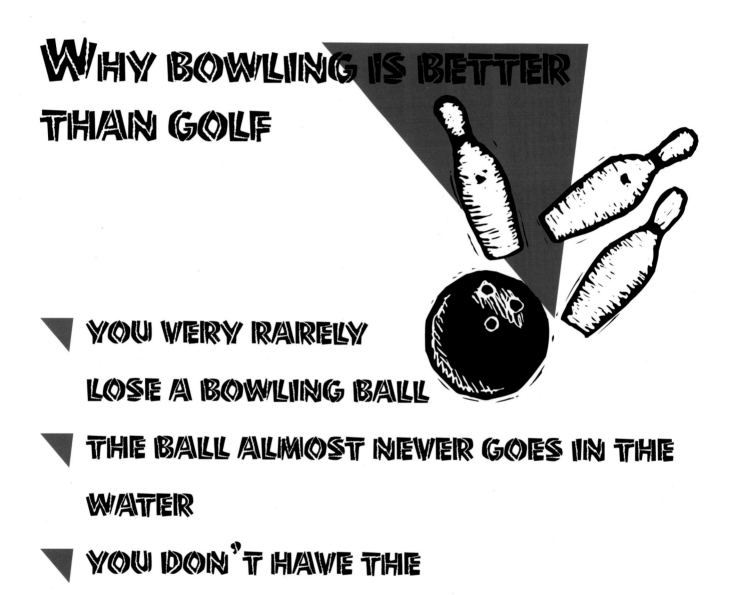

▼ YOU VERY RARELY LOSE A BOWLING BALL

▼ THE BALL ALMOST NEVER GOES IN THE WATER

▼ YOU DON'T HAVE THE EMBARRASSMENT OF YELLING "FORE" WHEN YOU GOOF UP

Shaman™ is a Fontek font from ITC

Personal

ABCDEFGHIJKLMNOPQRSTUVWXYZ

abcdefghijklmnopqrstuvwxyz1234567890

The school team had a rare distinction: the starting five all had scoring averages in double figures, and each of their I.Q. scores likewise had 2 digits.

Personal is available from Olduvai

Sinaloa

ABCDEFGHIJKLMNOPQRSTUVWXYZ
1234567890

LAME EXCUSES
_____
AT DOG SCHOOL

Sinaloa™ is a Fontek font from ITC

Tiranti Solid

ABCDEFGHIJKLMNOPQRSTUVWXYZ
abcdefghijklmnopqrstuvwxyz1234567890

The young woman's date was a nice person, but she knew that if a movie of her life were ever made, he would be listed in the credits as "second tall man."

Tiranti Solid™ is a Fontek font from ITC

Spooky

ABCDEFGHIJKLMNOPQRSTUVWXYZ
abcdefghijklmnopqrstuvwxyz1234567890

Favorite Dog
Fantasies No. 9

I walk over
beside this guy who
lives in my house, and lie down on
my back. Then, he starts scratching
my stomach, and doesn't
quit until I go to sleep.

Spooky™ is a Fontek font from ITC

Slipstream

ABCDEFGHIJKLMNOPQRSTUVWXYZ
1234567890

Slipstream™ is a Fontek font from ITC

ITC True Grit

ABCDEFGHIJKLMNOPQRSTUVWXYZ
1234567890

That unmeaning and abominable custom, swearing.

George Washington
Orders Against Profanity
in the Army

ITC True Grit™ is available from ITC

Superstar

ABCDEFGHIJKLMNOPQRSTUVWXYZ
1234567890

TEST YOUR BASEBALL I.Q.
MATCH THE NUMBER WITH THE PLAYER.

1

3

4

5

6

7

8

42

Ted Williams
Jackie Robinson
Babe Ruth
Lou Gehrig
Yogi Berra
Billy Martin
Joe Dimaggio
Stan Musial
Mickey Mantle

9

Answers: Ted Williams 9; Jackie Robinson 42; Babe Ruth 3; Lou Gehrig 4; Yogi Berra 8; Billy Martin 1; Joe Dimaggio 5; Stan Musial 6; Mickey Mantle 7.

Superstar™ is a Fontek font from ITC

Vegas

ABCDEFGHIJKLMNOPQRSTUVWXYZ
abcdefghijklmnopqrstuvwxyz1234567890

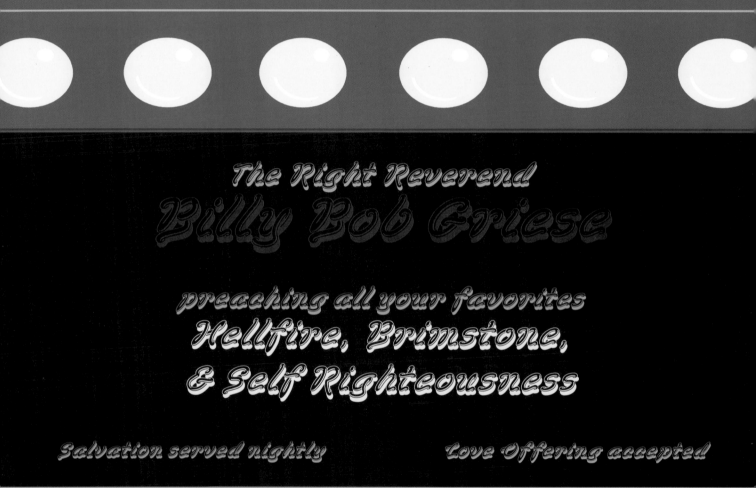

The Right Reverend
Billy Bob Griese

preaching all your favorites
Hellfire, Brimstone,
& Self Righteousness

Salvation served nightly   Love Offering accepted

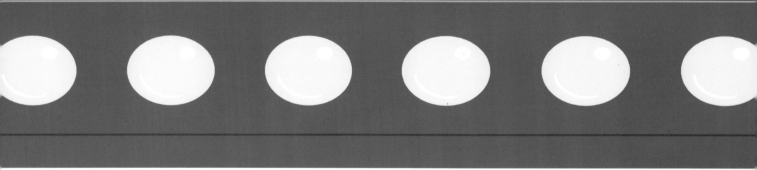

Vegas™ is a Fontek font from ITC

Westwood

ABCDEFGHIJKLMNOPQRSTUVWXYZ

abcdefghijklmnopqrstuvwxyz1234567890

Westwood™ is a Fontek font from ITC

Neo Neo

ABCDEFGHIJKLMNOPQRSTUVWXYZ
abcdefghijklmnopqrstuvwxyz1234567890

Favorite Dog Fantasies, No. 18

This **Hollywood producer** comes to my door and says, "People are getting TIRED of Lassie. We're thinking about a series starring a DALMATIAN! Would you like to be in the movies?"

Neo Neo™ is a Fontek font from ITC

Klee

ABCDEFGHIJKLMNOPQRSTUVWXYZ

abcdefghijklmnopqrstuvwxyz1234567890

bloom where you are planted

Klee™ is a Fontek font from ITC

Willow

ABCDEFGHIJKLMNOPQRSTUVWXYZ
1234567890

WALTER GOT SOME TALENTED FRIENDS
AND FORMED THE
VIENNA STRING QUINTET.

THEIR MUSIC WAS BEAUTIFUL,
EVEN IF THEIR MATH WAS
A LITTLE SUSPECT.

Willow™ is a Fontek font from ITC

Psycho

ABCDEFGHIJKLMNOPQRSTUVWXYZ
abcdefghijklmnopqrstuvwxyz1234567890

We have always known
that heedless self-interest
was bad morals; we now
know that it is bad economics.

Franklin Delano Roosevelt
Second Inaugural Address
(January 20, 1937)

Psycho is available from Olduvai

Westside

ABCDEFGHIJKLMNOPQRSTUVWXYZ
ABCDEFGHIJKLMNOPQRSTUVWXYZ1234567890

DON'T COMPLAIN ABOUT THE RAIN
UNTIL YOU'RE A THIRSTY MAN

Westside™ is a Fontek font from ITC

Vector

ABCDEFGHIJKLMNOPQRSTUVWXYZ
abcdefghijklmnopqrstuvwxyz1234567890

Vector Outline Bold

ABCDEFGHIJKLMNOPQRSTUVWXYZ
abcdefghijklmnopqrstuvwxyz1234567890

Is she Do YOU THINK I'M MADE OF MONEY?

Do you want to break your neck?

you

a What were you thinking?

Are you thinking

IF ALL YOUR FRIENDS JUMPED OFF A BRIDGE, WOULD YOU DO THAT, TOO?

hear

trying to heat

nice girl?

me?

the great outdoors?

Vector, Vector Bold, Vector Oblique & Vector Outline Bold are available from Aerotype

Mini Pics International

TFAkimbo Contrast-Medium

ABCDEFGHIJKLMNOPQRSTUVWXYZ

abcdefghijklmnopqrstuvwxyz 1234567890

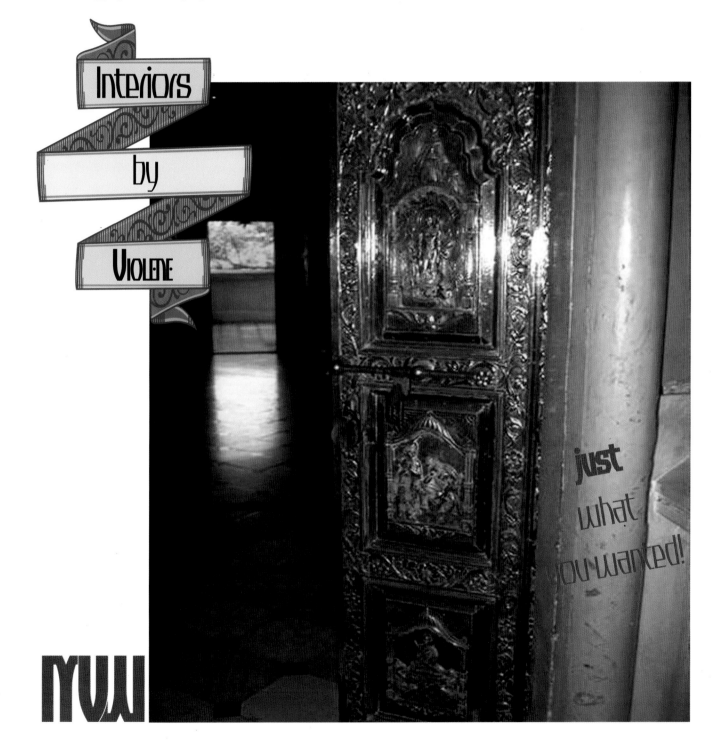

Interiors

by

Violene

just
what
you wanted!

TFAkimbo Contrast-Bold, TFAkimbo Contrast-Demibold, TFAkimbo Contrast-Extrabold TFAkimbo Contrast-Heavy, TFAkimbo Contrast-Light &TFAkimbo Contrast-Medium are available from Treacyfaces

Mini Pics Confetti Light

Psychological Image Testing		
image	reaction	analysis
	"My mommy."	mother has a bad case of crow's feet
	"Looks like sperm."	subject and wife are trying to have a baby without success; subject has feelings of inadequacy and questions his manhood
	"Opera."	the diva had a bad perm
	"Maybe a Stuart plaid."	subject has strong desire to wear a kilt
	"My boss's nose."	subject's employer has a big nose

Mini Pics Confetti Heavy, Mini Pics Confetti Light & Mini Pics Confetti Medium are available from Image Club

FrakturFont

ABCDEFGHIJKLMNOPQRSTUVWXYZ
abcdefghijklmnopqrstuvwxyz1234567890

Cultural History Lesson for Today

Scandinavian families had distinctive styles of knitting sweaters for their seafaring men.

Each family's knitting pattern made it easier to identify bodies of men who had drowned at sea.

FrakturFont is available from Image Club

Mini Pics Lil Vehicles

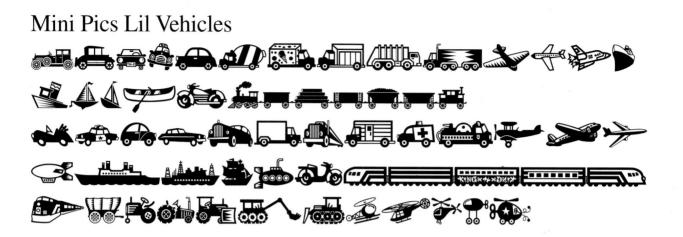

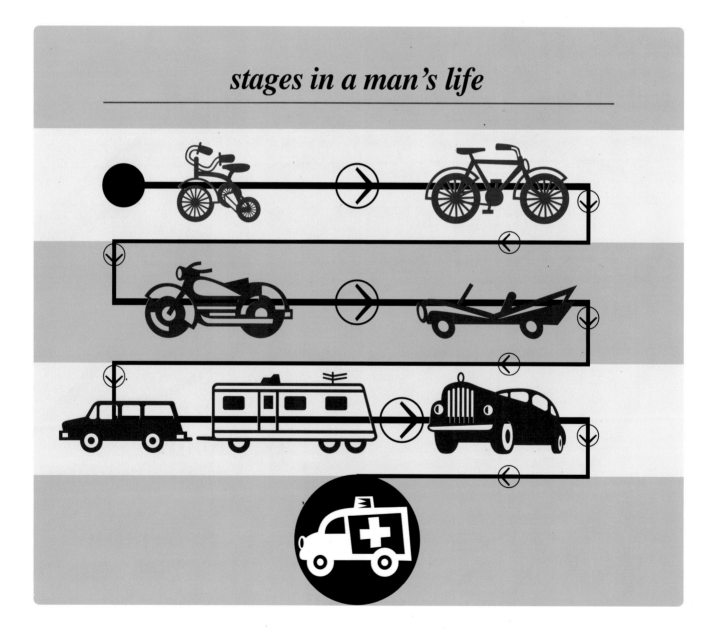

stages in a man's life

Mini Pics Lil Vehicles is available from Image Club

Carver ICG

ABCDEFGHIJKLMNOPQRSTUVWXYZ
abcdefghijklmnopqrstuvwxyz1234567890

Georgie Porgie, puddin' and pie, kissed the girls and made them cry.

When the boys came out to play, Georgie Porgie ran away.

Carver is available from Image Club

Regular Joe

ABCDEFGHIJKLMNOPQRSTUVWXYZ
abcdefghijklmnopqrstuvwxyz1234567890

An Unsolicited Testimonial

Much of the art in this book is from the Art Parts Collection. I liked the art so much, I even paid retail for most of it. (However, I shamelessly begged them to give their newer stuff to me as an act of kindness.) Anyway, Art Parts is a collection of illustrations for computers (or, more accurately, for people who use computers.) The illustrations above are typical of the Art Parts collection.

Anyway, Art Parts is a small (but highly creative) company run by two guys named Ron and Joe. (They didn't give their last names, and I didn't ask why. You can draw your own conclusions.)

If you like their art which appears in this book, think how good it will look on your stuff. The last page in this book tells where to get more information about their art. If you buy, be sure to tell them you saw it here. You won't get a discount, but it sure will make Ron and Joe feel better about the free stuff that they sent to me.

Regular Joe is available from Art Parts

Recycle-Standard

ABCDEFGHIJKLMNOPQRSTUVWXYZ
ABCDEFGHIJKLMNOPQRSTUVWXYZ
1234567890

Recycle-Alternate, Recycle-Alternate Reverse, Recycle-Outline, Recycle-Reverse & Recycle-Standard are available from Aerotype

Zinjaro

ABCDEFGHIJKLMNOPQRSTUVWXYZ
1234567890

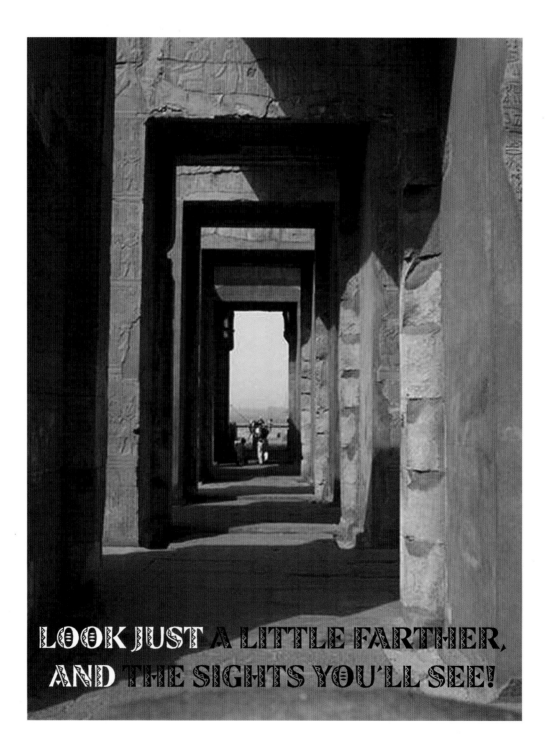

LOOK JUST A LITTLE FARTHER,
AND THE SIGHTS YOU'LL SEE!

Zinjaro is available from Fontek

Safari

ABCDEFGHIJKLMNOPQRSTUVWXYZ
ABCDEFGHIJKLMNOPQRSTUVWXYZ1234567890

TO: E.B. HAZLITT
FROM: R.W. LAMB
RE: BS (BUREAUCRATIC STRATEGEM, ETC.)

THREE CHANCELLORS VICE!
THREE CHANCELLORS VICE!
MEETINGS TO RUN!
MEETINGS TO RUN!
ADMINISTRATION TO OVERFLOW,
COMMITTEES COME, COMMITTEES GO,
DID YOU EVER SEE SUCH HOT AIR BLOW
AS THREE CHANCELLORS VICE?

Safari is available from Olduvai

LaBamba

ABCDEFGHIJKLMNOPQRSTUVWXYZ
abcdefghijklmnopqrstuvwxyz1234567890

The new invention that the world needs most is a heated water dish for dogs. It would run off electricity and keep the bowl warm enough to not let the water freeze over, but not so warm that it will get the water warm. Then people like me wouldn't have to go out in the winter and change their dog's water every hour.

John-michael Brown

LaBamba™ is a Fontek font from ITC

Zaragoza

ABCDEFGHIJKLMNOPQRSTUVWXYZ
abcdefghijklmnopqrstuvwxyz1234567890

The fear of
going to the
Emergency Room
with Dirty Underwear
has saved more lives than
the 55 miles per hour speed limit.

Mothers of America, we thank you.

ABCDEFGHIJKLMNOPQRSTUVWXYZ
abcdefghijklmnopqrstuvwxyz1234567890

Favorite Dog Fantasies—521

So I'm out for a walk with this guy
I own, and we see this great
looking bitch.
I say, "I love
the smell of
your perfume,
baby."

And she says, "Your place or mine?"

Then I notice that my guy isn't holding the
leash very tightly. And then I'm gone for
about two days.

Doggonit, it doesn't get any better than that.

Xylo™ is a Fontek font from ITC

Rollover

abcdefghijklmnopqrstuvwxyz
abcdefghijklmnopqrstuvwxyz1234567890

Rollover Outline

abcdefghijklmnopqrstuvwxyz
abcdefghijklmnopqrstuvwxyz1234567890

"the ideal size for a committee is 3 people. especially if the other 2 are never available for meetings."

overheard at harvard business school

Rollover & Rollover Outline are available from Mind Candy

Groovy

ABCDEFGHIJKLMNOPQRSTUVWXYZ
abcdefghijklmnopqrstuvwxyz1234567890

Groovy is available from Mind Candy

Delirium

ABCDEFGHIJKLMNOPQRSTUVWXYZ

abcdefghijklmnopqrstuvwxyz1234567890

Delirium is available from Mind Candy

Invacuo Cloak

ABCDEFGHIJKLMNOPQRSTUVWXYZ
abcdefghijklmnopqrstuvwxyz1234567890

All that we see
or seem
Is but a dream
within a dream.

E. A. Poe
A Dream
within a Dream

Invacuo Cloak is available from Mind Candy

Bureaucracy—Municipal
ABCDEFGHIJKLMNOPQRSTUVWXYZ
abcdefghijklmnopqrstuvwxyz1234567890

"Come to the edge" he said.

"We are afraid" they said.

"Come to the edge" he said.

They came.

He pushed them.

And they flew.

Bureaucracy is available in 3 weights from Mind Candy

Blind Faith

ABCDEFGHIJKLMNOPQRSTUVWXYZ
abcdefghijklmnopqrstuvwxyz1234567890

Have you ever been alone at night and heard silence so loud you thought your eardrums would burst?

Blind Faith is available from Mind Candy

Newtron ICG Regular

ABCDEFGHIJKLMNOPQRSTUVWXYZ
ABCDEFGHIJKLMNOPQRSTUVWXYZ
1234567890

Newtron ICG Open

ABCDEFGHIJKLMNOPQRSTUVWXYZ
ABCDEFGHIJKLMNOPQRSTUVWXYZ
1234567890

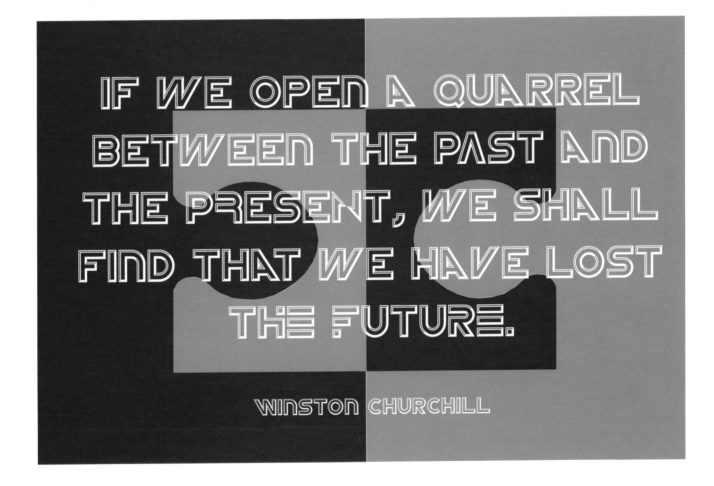

IF WE OPEN A QUARREL
BETWEEN THE PAST AND
THE PRESENT, WE SHALL
FIND THAT WE HAVE LOST
THE FUTURE.

WINSTON CHURCHILL

Newtron ICG is available from Image Club

133

Nucleus

ABCDEFGHIJKLMNOPQRSTUVWXYZ
ABCDEFGHIJKLMNOPQRSTUVWXYZ
1234567890

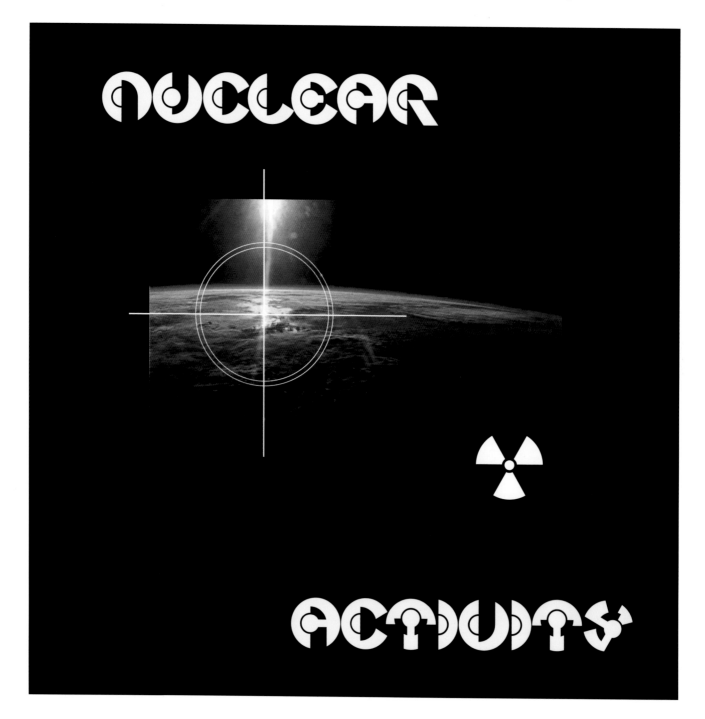

Nucleus is available from Mind Candy

Sibley Potato Fried

ABCDEFGHIJKLMNOPQRSTUVWXYZ
abcdefghijklmnopqrstuvwxyz1234567890

Sibley Potato Mashed

ABCDEFGHIJKLMNOPQRSTUVWXYZ
abcdefghijklmnopqrstuvwxyz1234567890

Poetry sang
in his eyes . . .

but those thoughts
are piercing
and dead none
         on for
pain's sake.

Sibley Potato Baked, Sibley Potato Fried & Sibley Potato Mashed are available from Mind Candy

jobless

ABCDEFGHIJKLMNOPQRSTUVWXYZ
abcdefghijklmnopqrstuvwxyz1234567890

The Dog
National Anthem

While I lie here slee-ping
getting rubbed on the ear,
I give thanks for my home
and the people who live here.
Cats may have kitty lit-ter
and beds made from
velvet rags,
But only in the U.S.
do they have doggy bags.

jobless is available from Mind Candy

Missing Link

ABCDEFGHIJKLMNOP&RSTUVWXYZ
abcdefghijklmnopqrstuvwxyz1234567890

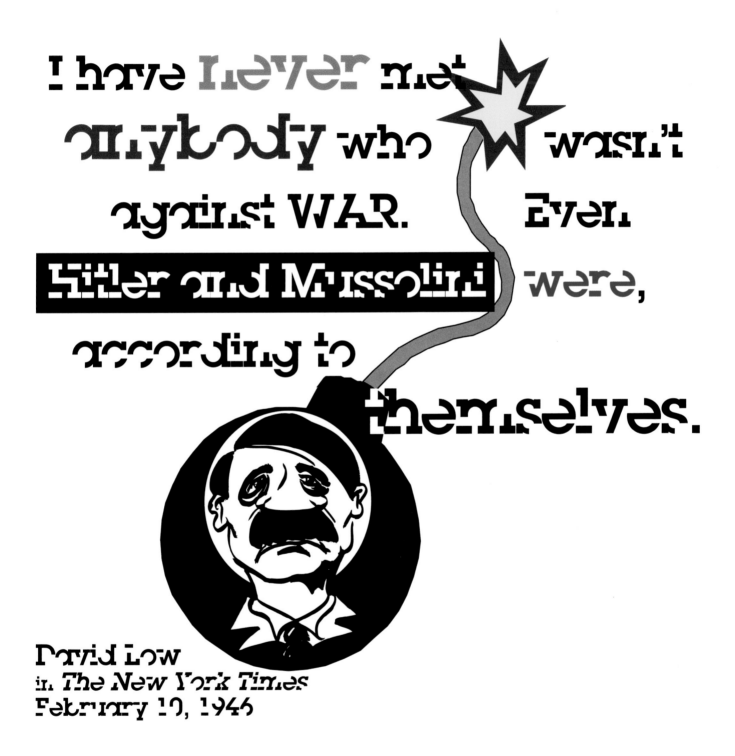

I have never met anybody who wasn't against WAR. Even Hitler and Mussolini were, according to themselves.

David Low
in *The New York Times*
February 10, 1946

Missing Link is available from Mind Candy

Joker

abcdefghijklmnopqrstuvwxyz
abcdefghijklmnopqrstuvwxyz1234567890

Joker is available from Mind Candy

Faith

ABCDEFGHIJKLMNOPQRSTUVWXYZ
abcdefghijklmnopqrstuvwxyz1234567890

Some one invented the telephone,
And interrupted a nation's
slumbers,

Ogden Nash
Look What You Did, Christopher

Ringing
wrong
but
similar
numbers.

Faith is available from Mind Candy

Slacker-Bookstore

ABCDEFGHIJKLMNOPQRSTUVWXYZ
abcdefghijklmnopqrstuvwxyz1234567890

Bleed for us, Beauty, and cry no tears of passion for the whore of love and youth.

Slacker-Bookstore is available from Mind Candy

Gonza

ABCDEFGHIJKLMNOPQRSTUVWXYZ

abcdefghijklmnopqrstuvwxyz1234567890

Gonza Bold

ABCDEFGHIJKLMNOPQRSTUVWXYZ

abcdefghijklmnopqrstuvwxyz1234567890

Favorite Dog Fantasies, #117

This guy who lives in my house is cooking 6 big steaks on the grill. He **burns** them just enough so that people won't like them. Then he hollers, "Hey Buster. Come here!"

Gonza is available from 2 Rebels

Cuty

ABCDEFGHIJKLMNOPQRSTUVWXYZ

abcdefghijklmnopqrstuvwxyz1234567890

Hallmark doesn't make cards for these occasions...

I'm sorry your boa constrictor escaped and terrorized the neighbors.

We extend our sympathy upon the occasion of your parole being revoked

CONGRATULATIONS for appearing on the daytime talk show and exposing your stupidity to an entire nation.

Cuty is available from 2 Rebels

Clean Cut-Caps

ABCDEFGHIJKLMNOPQRSTUVWXYZ
ABCDEFGHIJKLMNOPQRSTUVWXYZ1234567890

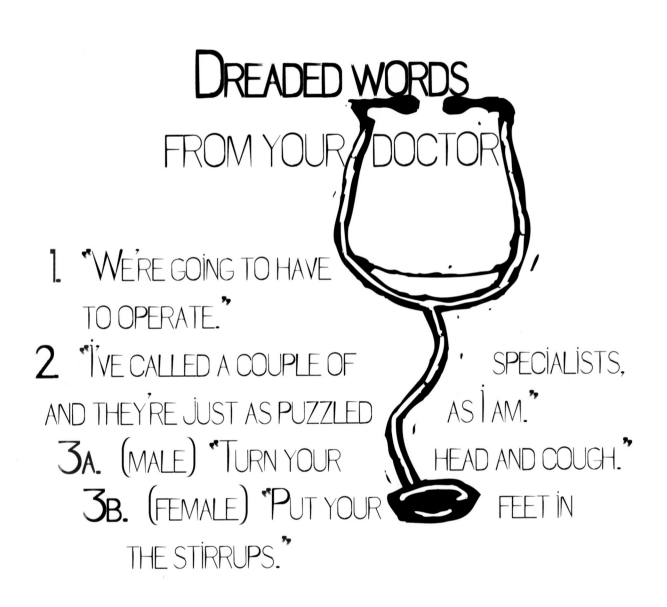

DREADED WORDS

FROM YOUR DOCTOR

1. "WE'RE GOING TO HAVE TO OPERATE."

2. "I'VE CALLED A COUPLE OF SPECIALISTS, AND THEY'RE JUST AS PUZZLED AS I AM."

3A. (MALE) "TURN YOUR HEAD AND COUGH."

3B. (FEMALE) "PUT YOUR FEET IN THE STIRRUPS."

Clean Cut is available from 2 Rebels

Luna Martino-Grossa

ABCDEFGHIJKLMNOPQRSTUVWXYZ
abcdefghijklmnopqrstuvwxyz1234567890

This bank called me in and asked me to create a new logo. "Animals seem to make good logos," they said. "But we want an animal that nobody else has used."

So, a week later, I came back with a proposal. "Here it is," I said proudly.

Greenup County Bank

"What kind of animal is that?" they asked.

"An Amoeba," I said.

They went with another designer.

Luna Martino-Grosso is available from 2 Rebels

Manomessa

ABCDEFGHIJKLMNOPQRSTUVWXYZ
abcdefghijklmnopqrstuvwxyz1234567890

Manomessa-Bucata

ABCDEFGHIJKLMNOPQRSTUVWXYZ
abcdefghijklmnopqrstuvwxyz1234567890

If Psychiatrists were marketing-oriented:

SPECIAL THIS WEEK

LOWER PRICES

40% off

for all Anal-Rententive Disorders

Manomessa and Manomessa Bucata are available from 2 Rebels

Voyou

ABCDEFGHIJKLMNOPQRSTUVWXYZ
abcdefghijklmnopqrstuvwxyz1234567890

In the 1950s, the "bad kids" were punished for bringing one of these to school.

Today, the slingshot is the least of our worries.

Mutation

ABCDEFGHIJKLMNOPQRSTUVWXYZ
abcdefghijklmnopqrstuvwxyz1234567890

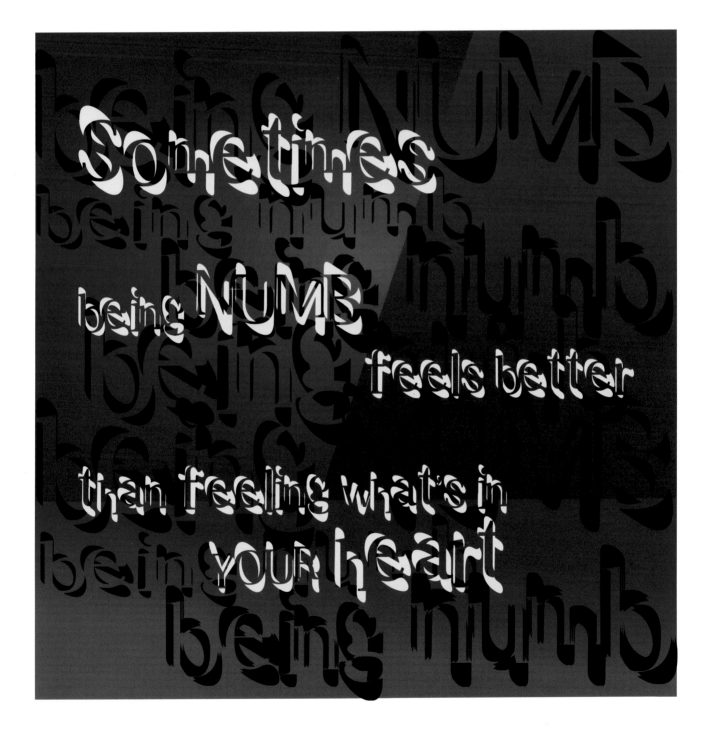

Mutation is available from 2 Rebels

Vague

ABCDEFGHIJKLMNOPQRSTUVWXYZ
abcdefghijklmnopqrstuvwxyz1234567890

Vague Outline

ABCDEFGHIJKLMNOPQRSTUVWXYZ
abcdefghijklmnopqrstuvwxyz1234567890

If it's late at night...

If you're all alone...

If you want to talk...

Whatever you want...

Call Rochelle

1-900-WET-****

$4.95 first minute
$1.50 each additional minute

Vague is available from 2 Rebels

Semi Sans

ABCDEFGHIJKLMNOPQRSTUVWXYZ

abcdefghijklmnopqrstuvwxyz1234567890

"It is our true policy to steer clear of permanent alliances with any portion of the foreign world."

George Washington
Farewell Address
September 17, 1796

Semi Sans is available from 2 Rebels

South - Rounded

ABCDEFGHIJKLMNOPQRSTUVWXYZ
abcdefghijklmnopqrstuvwxyz1234567890

South - Outline

ABCDEFGHIJKLMNOPQRSTUVWXYZ
abcdefghijklmnopqrstuvwxyz1234567890

The play left the taste of lukewarm parsnip juice.

Alexander Woollcott

drama review in
The New York Times

South is available from 2 Rebels

150

Menace

abcdefghijklmnopqrstuvwxyz
abcdefghijklmnopqrstuvwxyz1234567890

Menace is available from 2 Rebels

Razzia

ABCDEFGHIJKLMNOPQRSTUVWXYZ

abcdefghijklmnopqrstuvwxyz1234567890

PIECEMAKERS
Quilt & Needle Arts Shop

proudly announces its association
with quilting expert

Betty Lou

Razzia is available from 2 Rebels

Scritto Politto Freako

ABCDEFGHIJKLMNOPQRSTUVWXYZ
abcdefghijklmnopqrstuvwxyz
1234567890

dumb things you don't want to say

When your
fellow
workers are
talking about
tough golf
holes,
don't say:

"I really have trouble getting the ball past the
windmill and into the clown's mouth."

Toxin-Spotless

ABCDEFGHIJKLMNOPQRSTUVWXYZ
abcdefghijklmnopqrstuvwxyz1234567890

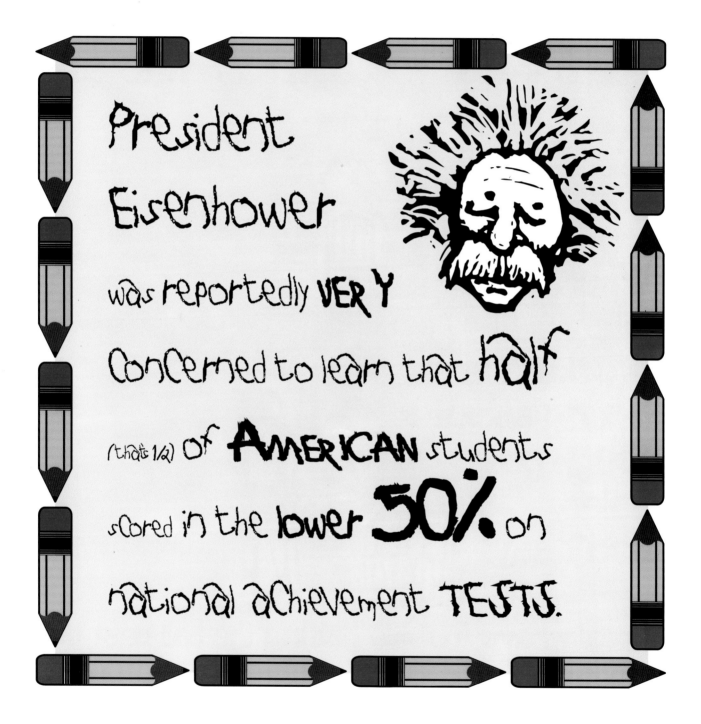

President Eisenhower was reportedly VERY concerned to learn that half (that 1/2) of AMERICAN students scored in the lower 50% on national achievement TESTS.

Toxin-Spotless is available from 2 Rebels

Mini Pics Lil Ancients

Mini Pics Lil Ancients is available from Image Club

Sofa

abcdefghijklmnopqrstuvwxyz1234567890

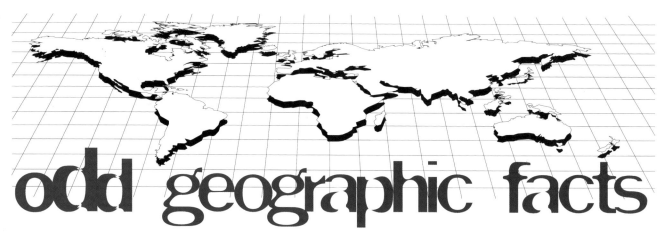

odd geographic facts

(they're all true-you can look it up)

-- reno, nevada is farther west than los angeles

-- if you go directly south from cincinnati, ohio, you'll reach the pacific ocean

-- there is no florida

(well, 2 out of 3 are true)

Sofa is available from 2 Rebels

Thin Man

ABCDEFGHIJKLMNOPQRSTUVWXYZ
ABCDEFGHIJKLMNOPQRSTUVWXYZ
1234567890

Thin Man - Drunk

ABCDEFGHIJKLMNOPQRSTUVWXYZ
ABCDEFGHIJKLMNOPQRSTUVWXYZ
1234567890

MAY I SEE YOUR DRIVER'S LICENSE?

WHAT FOR OFFICER?

YOUR DRIVER'S LICENSE – PLEASE.

WHAT FOR officer?

WHINING WILL GET THREE ADDITIONAL
POINTS OFF YOUR LICENSE.

Thin Man is available from 2 Rebels

Nameless

ABCDEFGHIJKLMNOPQRSTUVWXYZ
abcdefghijklmnopqrstuvwxyz1234567890

Nameless - Bold

ABCDEFGHIJKLMNOPQRSTUVWXYZ
abcdefghijklmnopqrstuvwxyz1234567890

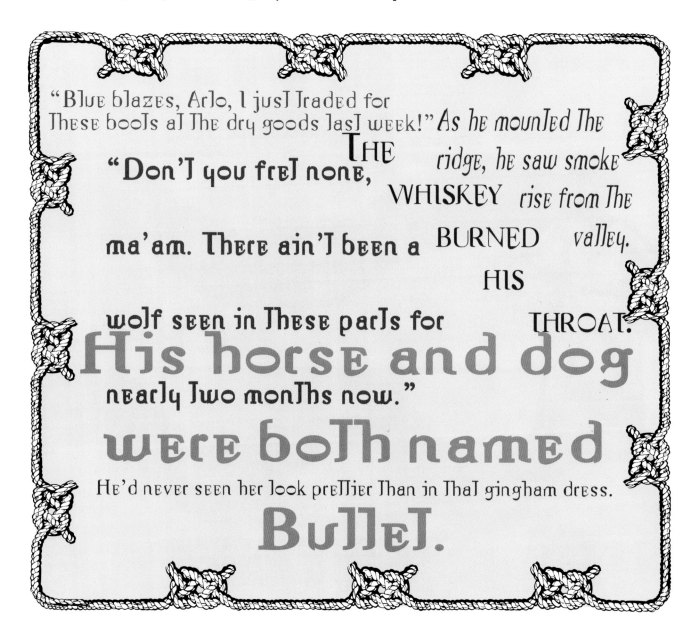

"Blue blazes, Arlo, I just traded for these boots at the dry goods last week!" As he mounted the THE ridge, he saw smoke WHISKEY rise from the

"Don't you fret none, ma'am. There ain't been a BURNED valley. HIS

wolf seen in these parts for THROAT. His horse and dog nearly two months now." were both named He'd never seen her look prettier than in that gingham dress. Bullet.

Nameless is available from 2 Rebels

Quattrocchi

ABCDEFGHIJKLMNOPQRSTUVWXYZ
abcdefghijklmnopqrstuvwxyz1234567890

Two Questions about Penguins

What does a penguin wear to a formal affair?

and

Do penguins have a "dress casual" day?

Quattrocchi is available from 2 Rebels

Plastic Man

ABCDEFGHI JKLMNOPQRSTUVWXYZ

ABCDEFGHI JKLMNOPQRSTUVWXYZ1234567890

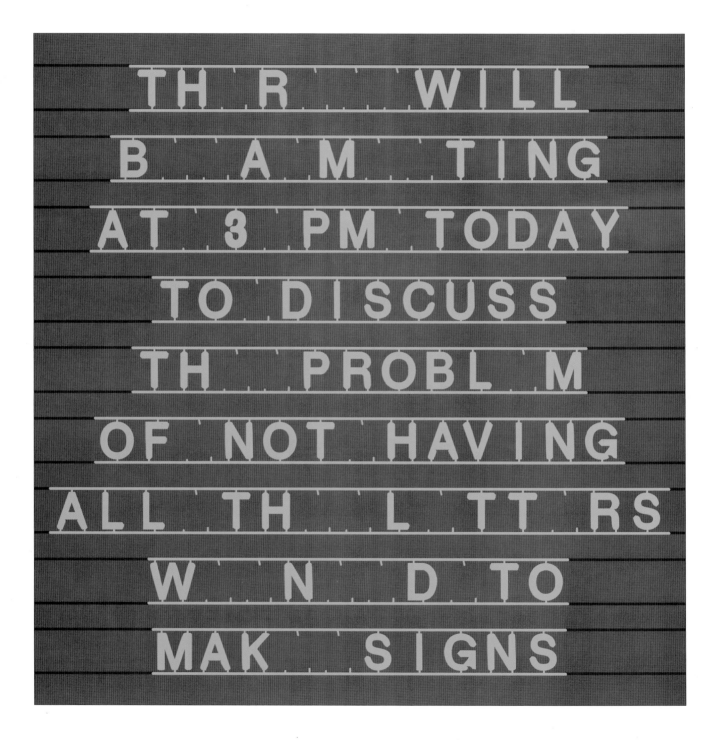

Plastic Man is available from 2 Rebels

Nunavik

ᐊᑉᑕᐤᐁᖕᕐᖄᕼᒐᒃᑕᒪᒥᑎᐅᕆᕈᕐᑌᑐᐺᐳᒴᑐᓐ1234567890

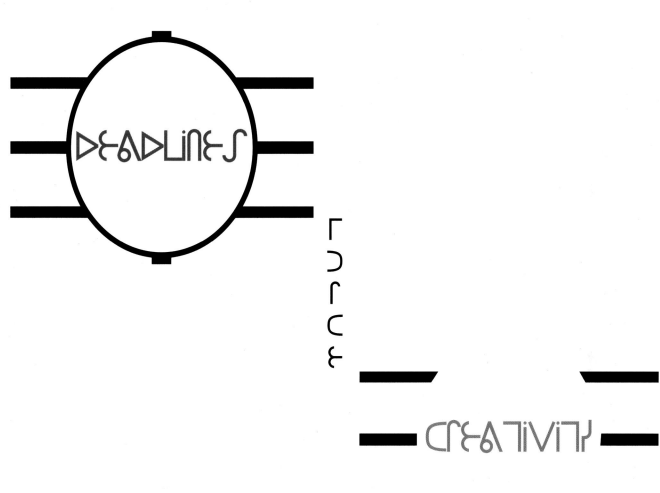

Nunavik is available from 2 Rebels.

Nonlinear Open

ABCDEFGHIJKLMNOPQRSTUVWXYZ
abcdefghijklmnopqrstuvwxyz
1234567890

Nonlinear Solid

ABCDEFGHIJKLMNOPQRSTUVWXYZ
abcdefghijklmnopqrstuvwxyz
1234567890()

Nonlinear Open & Nonlinear Solid are available from 2 Rebels

RockaBilly ICG

ABCDEFGHIJKLMNOPQRSTUVVXYZ
abcdefghijklmnopqrstuvvxyz
1234567890

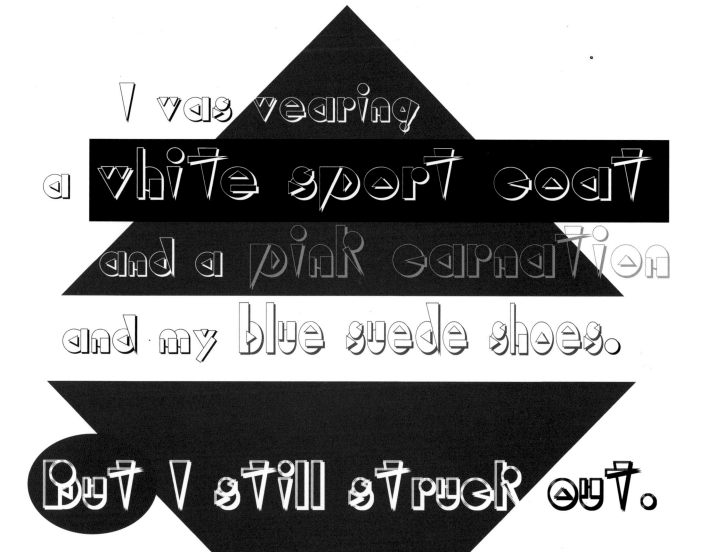

I was wearing a white sport coat and a pink carnation and my blue suede shoes. But I still struck out.

RockaBilly is available from Image Club

Manesca

ABCDEFGHIJKLMNOPQRSTUVWXYZ

abcdefghijklmnopqrstuvwxyz1234567890

How advertising history was almost changed.

There was once an advertising writer who had a great idea for a headline. It might have been the best ad headline of all time.

He knew that it would win awards, praise, and a promotion. He quickly sketched it on a bar napkin.

Then, he sat his glass of bourbon on the rocks on the napkin.

The melting ice made the headline turn into a blob. The next morning, the writer didn't even remember writing a headline.

Manesca is available from 2 Rebels

Café Noir

ABCDEFGHIJKLMNOPQRSTUVWXYZ
abcdefghijklmnopqrstuvwxyz1234567890

"You're cute as a bug's ear," he said. "Though I don't really know what a bug's ear looks like. Maybe it's an antenna.

"Do you think it's an antenna?

"You're cute as a bug's antenna," he said, silver-tongued devil that he was.

That relationship never quite developed.

Café Noir is available from 2 Rebels

Carbon Regular

ABCDEFGHIJKLMNOPQRSTUVWXYZ
ABCDEFGHIJKLMNOPQRSTUVWXYZ1234567890

LITTLE-KNOWN FACT ABOUT DOGS

Q. WHY DO DOGS CHASE CATS?

A. ITS ACTUALLY A GAME. THE CAT IS PRETENDING TO BE A SPEEDING MOTORIST, AND THE DOG IS PRETENDING TO BE THE SHERIFF.

Carbon Regular is available from 2 Rebels

Nacht

ABCDEFGHIJKLMNOPQRSTUVWXYZ

abcdefghijklmnopqrstuvwxyz**1234567890**

Dr. Katz--Veterinarian

Doghouse Improvement

8 minutes and 34 seconds
(that's 60 Minutes in dog years)

Favorite Dog TV Shows

Nacht is available from 2 Rebels

Greco - In

ABCDEFGHIJKLMNOPQRSTUVWXYZ

ABCDEFGHIJKLMNOPQRSTUVWXYZ

1234567890

Greco-In is available from 2 Rebels

Junk

ABCDEFGHIJKLMNOPQRSTUVWXYZ
abcdefghijklmnopqrstuvwxyz1234567890

I gave myself away
and that's okay,
but I didn't get me
back...

Now I'm by myself.
I'm talking to
myself.
I'm great company,
but I'm lonely.

Junk is available from 2 Rebels

Babbio Alto

ABCDEFGHIJKLMNOPQRSTUVWXYZ1234567890

Babbio Basso

ABCDEFGHIJKLMNOPQRSTUVWXYZ1234567890

Babbio Alto & Babbio Basso are available from 2 Rebels

Dclite

ABCDEFGHIJKLMNOPQRSTUVWXYZ

abcdefghijklmnopqrstuvwxyz1234567890

You can't buy this font, because it's my (Dave Carter's) handwriting.

(Flashback to my childhood, with someone shouting "it's mine! it's mine!")

This is my own personal font, and you can have your own font, too.

I put this page in for 2 reasons:

1. I really think it's neat to have your own font.
2. We needed just one more font to fill up the book.

(This is another unsolicited testimonial. Nobody at Signature Software asked me to do it.)

It's mine!
It's mine

Personal Pen Fonts are available from Signature Software

Boggle

ABCDEFGHIJKLMNOPQRSTUVWXYZ
abcdefghijklmnopqrstuvwxyz1234567890

The real revenge of the nerds

Remember the quiet guy who wore a plastic pocket protector in high school?

At the 20-year class reunion, he'll come back with his Ph.D. from MIT. And everybody will be talking about how he invented the Whazzit®, his company went public, and he's a gazillionnaire.

(Meanwhile, the jocks who used to taunt him will be over in the corner with their beer bellies, reliving the best days of their lives.)

Boggle is available from 2 Rebels

2 RebelsDeux- Regular

ABCDEFGHIJKLMNOPQRSTUVWXYZ
abcdefghijklmnopqrstuvwxyz1234567890

2 RebelsDeux- Bold

ABCDEFGHIJKLMNOPQRSTUVWXYZ
abcdefghijklmnopqrstuvwxyz1234567890

Why there
are no
famous dog singers

- dogs have a limited octave range
- dogs don't buy CD's
- the best songwriters don't understand the language

2 Rebels is available from 2 Rebels

1Proton - 1

abcdefghijklmnopqrstuvwxyz1234567890

2Proton - 2

abcdefghijklmnopqrstuvwxyz1234567890

lines that
neil armstrong
possibly
considered
–and
rejected

- "so–where's the green cheese!"
- "hi, mom!"
- "since i'm the first person here, does that mean i can be king!"

1Proton 1 & 2Proton 2 are available from 2 Rebels

TFGary-Medium

ABCDEFGHIJKLMNOPQRSTUVWXYZ

abcdefghijklmnopqrstuvwxyz 1234567890

The Lunch Box

What Jimmy's mom packed

- Ham sandwich with lettuce & tomato
- skim milk (1/2 pint)
- Pear
- Apple

What Jimmy wished his mom had packed

- Peanut butter sandwich, with grape jelly & banana
- Pepsi (20 oz.)
- Snickers bar
- Reese's Peanut Butter Cup
- M & M's (large)

TFGary-Medium is available from Treacyfaces

WHERE TO BUY FONTS SHOWN IN THIS BOOK

If you're a font lover, by now you're probably frothing at the mouth and wanting to add some of these designs to your personal collection.

If that's the case, we've made it very easy for you. Below is a list of firms offering fonts shown in the book, with addresses and phones for your convenience.

Aerotype   501 W. Glenoaks Blvd., #523, Glendale, California 91202. Phone: (818) 841-7120. Fax: (818) 843-7153.

Art Parts   Box 2926, Orange, California 92669-0926. Phone: (714) 771-6754. Fax: (714) 633-9617.

Coniglio Typefonts USA   124 Woodside Green 2B, Stamford, CT 06905. Phone: (800) 484-1258 #3489. Fax: (203) 967-3123.

Great American Font Works: Silver Graphics, 307 W. Morgan Avenue, Pennington Gap, Virginia 24277. Phone: (540) 546-3800. Fax: (540) 546-2380.

Image Club   10545 West Donges Court, Milwaukee, Wisconsin 53224-9967. Orders: (800) 387-9193. Catalog Requests: (800) 661-9410. Fax: (800) 814-7783.

ITC (International Typeface Corporation) distributes its fonts through several resellers including:

Adobe	(800) 294-1724	Monotype	(800) 666-6897
AGFA	(508) 658-5600	Precision Type	(800) 248-3668
Bitstream	(617) 497-6222	TYPE USA	(800) TYPE USA
FontHaus	(800) 942-9110	FontShop International (Berlin)	011 49 30 69 58 95
Image Club	(800) 661-9410	FontWorks (UK)	011 44 171 490 5390

Mind Candy   1712 E. Riverside, Suite 88, Austin, TX 78741. Phone: (512) 448-3955. Fax: (512) 448-3760.

Olduvai Corporation   9200 South Dadeland Blvd., Suite 725, Miami, Florida 33156. Phone: (305) 670-1112. Fax: (305) 670-1992.

Signature Software, Inc.   489 N. 8th Street, Suite 201, Hood River, Oregon 97031. Phone: (800) 925-8840 or (541) 386-3221. Fax: (541) 386-3229.

Treaceyfaces, Inc.   P.O. Box 26036, West Haven, CT 06516-8036. Phone: (203) 389-7073.

2 Rebels   4623 Harvard, Montreal, Québec, Canada H4A 2X3. Phone: (514) 481-0984. Fax (514) 486-8657.